THE CINNABAR TOOLKIT
FOR COUNSELLORS
Volume I

By Toni Close and Mo Smith

Published in the United Kingdom by
Therapy Professional Press, an imprint of:

Cinnabar Training
19 Gloucester Road, Stamford
Lincolnshire, PE9 1LH UK.
www.cinnabartraining.com

First edition printed January 2016

ISBN 978-0-9934570-0-5

The case studies and clients named in this book are fictitious, based on aspects of actual client stories and experiences with the worksheets/paper tools. Any resemblance to real persons, living or dead, is entirely coincidental.

Although every precaution has been taken in the preparation of this book, the publisher and authors assume no responsibility for errors or omissions. Neither is any liability assumed for damages resulting from the use of the information, worksheets/paper tools contained herein.

Most images were sourced from www.openclipart.org.
The image used on *Who has the power?* was purchased from Adobe Stock Images.

About the publisher

Cinnabar Training is a family business run by mother and daughter. It was created to provide training workshops for counselling professionals and support workers, and now publishes non-fiction books for counsellors under the imprint: "Therapy Professional Press".

About the authors

Mo Smith is a senior accredited counsellor and supervisor with an extraordinary breadth of experience. In addition to having a well-established private practice, she works in a prison, organising counselling for inmates and coordinating volunteer counsellors. She also works with teenagers and children in local schools.

Mo is a qualified teacher and has past experience of teaching counselling courses from introductory to degree level as well as Level 5 CBT courses. The Cinnabar workshops benefit from case studies drawn from this extensive experience, as well as her incredible patience.

Toni Close is a freelance writer and researcher with a background in psychology and publishing. She has had a varied and interesting career as a research consultant during which she developed her natural talents for interviewing clients, designing communication tools and writing for a diverse audience.

A qualified teacher, she designs and creates the Cinnabar workshop materials, and facilitates the workshops alongside her mum.

Contents

Introduction

In counselling, tools are sometimes used to help clients to identify, explore, understand or process their thoughts and feelings.

Worksheets and other paper-based tools take thoughts and feelings out of a client's head and put them onto paper where they can be viewed with some perspective, or where they can be worked with, acknowledged or transformed.

They can be applied to a broad range of issues - from looking at someone's childhood or exploring their relationships, to talking through stress at work or working through grief.

Clients who struggle with reading and writing benefit from the clear images and underlying metaphors, while some clients (particularly younger clients) intuitively welcome the opportunity to work on something concrete.

Despite a tendency to associate paper-based tools with Cognitive Behavioural Therapy, they can also be used within a number of other therapeutic approaches such as psychodynamic, person-centred, transactional analysis, gestalt, existential, and holistic.

This book contains 20 diverse ready to use paper-based tools that can be used for a wide range of therapeutic issues, clients and counselling contexts.

Sometimes clients find it difficult to visualise their situation. They may see only part of their situation, or struggle to cope with a confusing or overwhelming impression of their problems. Tools such as *Mindmap, Timeline*, and *What are you carrying around?* encourage clients to map out the entire picture. This can be essential before realistic solutions can be considered. *Letting stress out, How I feel when…* and *Remembering* also work by asking the client to consider all the factors or qualities in each case.

Some tools work by using symbolism to help the client to understand their problem. For example, *What are you carrying around?* and *Letting stress out* use the ideas of "putting down" and "releasing pressure" as metaphors to deal with stress. Other tools in this book which use metaphor are: *Anchors* and *What's beneath your anger?*. *Things from the past...* and *Remembering* encourage the client to release painful memories by first putting them into metaphorical containers.

Tools like *Me and me, Blame & Fault, Child parent, Adult parent* and *Relationship changes* are designed to explore a specific issue in some detail. This type of tool usually provides a structure for the client to fill in that forces them to question or transform their viewpoint, and try to come to a new understanding.

Some tools in this book are particularly appropriate for clients who have a history of abuse, none more so than *Who has the power?*. This tool includes an element of symbolism in the representative figures that are portrayed, and also presents a question to the client that can have a huge therapeutic impact.

Sometimes clients benefit from putting their thoughts, intentions and ideas onto paper in order to produce something physical or concrete. This can then be referred to, embellished, and added to; even screwed up into a tiny ball or burned to produce a cathartic sense of release. A piece of paper can also be pinned to the wall, put on the fridge door, or carried around in a purse or wallet to remind the client of their thoughts, ideas and intentions. *Where are the people in my life?*, *Anchors*, *Remembering* and *Worry Tickets* are examples of tools that are often kept in a visible place. *Things from the past...* is a working document that can be physically altered as therapy progresses, and potentially act as a prompt for a physical ritual.

Finally, some tools guide clients to work through a problem, filling in boxes or following arrows and moving through a process. This might be in order to make a decision or identify a course of action. *Moving on from my regret*, *I'm giving up...* and *Making a decision* fall into this category, as does *Creating a STRIPE goal* (our approach created specifically for setting personal goals).

⬡ **Cinnabar**

All of the tools mentioned in this introduction are presented in the pages that follow, along with guidance on their use and fictitious case study examples.

We encourage you to use the worksheets and tools in this book in your practice (although please note the copyright and usage notes at the start of this book) and to get in touch with any feedback you may have via our website:

http:\\www.cinnabartraining.com

Before you start, here are some tips for using these tools:

SEVEN TOP TIPS FOR USING TOOLS

- Think carefully about what you are trying to achieve before you choose the tool.

- Consider whether the tool is appropriate at this point in your client's therapy. Are they ready for it?

- Match the tool to the client – some people are more receptive to different approaches.

- Be flexible – clients may cross out or alter labels. The tools don't have to be filled in perfectly.

- If you are sending the client home with a tool, go through the task with them. Explain why you are asking them to do this, and what you are hoping they might achieve.

- After the client has completed the tool, go through it with them. Discuss possible interpretations and ask them how they felt about doing the exercise. Link it to ongoing work in your sessions.

- If you fill in a tool during a session with a client, use their words not yours. They should always have ownership of the work.

- When you use more than one tool with a client, work through each exercise in turn. Leave some breathing room in between.

Cinnabar

1.

Mindmap

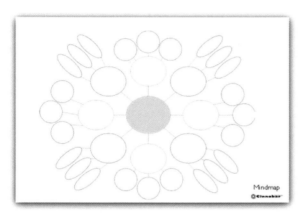

A Mindmap is a diagram that organises information by showing related thoughts, feelings, memories and facts radiating out from a central theme.

They can be created using guide templates like the one in this book, or they can be drawn entirely freehand with the added benefit of being totally free to expand in any direction. It is a skill that improves with practice.

Counsellors and support workers can use a Mindmap to record and organise information regarding a client's complex family structure and history, for example, or their unique pattern of health issues and sources of stress.

One way to use the tool provided in this book is to begin by labelling the central bubble with an issue or problem, event or person's name. Then label offshoots from that bubble with related thoughts, feelings, events or ideas. Continue labelling outward – each time recording ideas that are related to the previous bubble – until you have exhausted each pathway.

Mindmaps can also be drawn as a collaborative exercise during the session, or taken away by clients to complete as a piece of homework. This might be:

- to map out a particular issue for further discussion in the next session (for example, mapping 'my worries about work')

- as an ongoing progress tool where the client maps out their perceptions of the road travelled in each session (e.g. mapping 'what happened in this week's session')

- as a journal tool where the client chronicles their experiences with difficult settings (e.g. mapping 'dinner with parents')

The power of a Mindmap is in its ability to cluster information. This can be indicated by related information coming from the same bubble, or it might be shown by colouring linked bubbles. Mindmaps can also indicate groups and links with little pictures, stickers or emoticons.

Mindmaps can be created with any issue in mind, they are not limited to particular questions or perspectives, and the act of making a Mindmap is as useful as the finished Mindmap itself. As you write in the connected bubbles and draw your links, notes and arrows in the available space, you are working with the information in a way that your mind instinctively understands.

Case study: Sarah came to counselling because her home life was causing her a great deal of stress. She was in the process of divorcing her husband of 35 years and family members were choosing sides.

I started drawing a Mindmap so I could get my head around the complex family alliances she was describing. She watched fascinated as I drew in the bubbles branching from each issue into another cluster of connected family names. She began to tell me where to write and what to put. I gave her the sheet and told her to take it home and finish it.

At our next session, she presented a new extended version of the Mindmap. What had begun as a simple family Mindmap was now an emotional minefield in a rainbow of colours. The colours related to how Sarah thought each family member felt about her. I could immediately see pockets of orange, signifying allies in otherwise cold blue family clusters.

We referred back to this Mindmap many times during our sessions and I found it an invaluable aid to understanding Sarah's world.

Cinnabar

2.

Things from the past

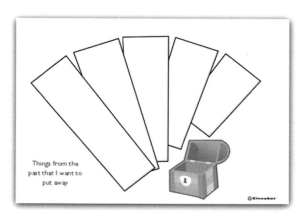

Things from the
past that I want to
put away

We are made from memories. Some of these are positive and hopeful, and remind us to continue moving forward with confidence in ourselves. Others are dark and painful, weighing us down with their lessons and messages.

Clients often come to counselling with a range of memories and emotions from their past that they want to work through, with the aim of reaching some kind of personal resolution and putting these things behind them.

This tool provides an effective way of structuring this process, with an easy metaphor.

First of all, write down the deep-seated issues that your client wants to deal with on the tool. These might all be apparent at the very first session, or may emerge after a little more time. By putting them on the tool, your client is identifying their intention to "put these issues away".

This does not mean that the issue will be resolved in any practical sense – usually this exercise involves traumas or unhappy memories that cannot be erased. Instead the aim is to reach a point where your client can decide that the memory will no longer have a distracting or upsetting effect on their daily lives. They can acknowledge that these memories exist, but then make a conscious decision to put them away and move forward with their lives.

After each issue has been explored – when your client feels that they have reached a suitable end-point – they can imagine putting the associated memories and feelings into a big box or chest and locking it away. They might cross out or colour that entry on the tool.

Some clients like to carry out this process for real, writing down their final thoughts on a particular subject and then putting it away into a real box or chest or safe in their home. Post-its can also be used quite effectively. The client fills in a post-it note for each issue and sticks them to a piece of paper. As each issue is dealt with, the post-its can be moved.

The tool starts off as a roadmap for the issues that the client will discuss in the sessions, and then shows the progress they have made as they deal with their unwanted past.

Case study: Nicola's husband had left her for another woman. She was now a single parent of two young children. When she came to counselling Nicola said that she acknowledged the fact that she was partly to blame for the breakup. As a result, she said that she had decided to deal with aspects of her past. She said: "I'm ready to get rid of some ghosts". We identified one of her "ghosts" to be the care home she had lived in as a child. This was the source of some strong emotions and feelings of "not belonging" and "not trusting".

Over time we explored what happened, how Nicola had felt, and how it affected her life now. One day Nicola said "it was never something I could control, was it?" She decided she was ready to put it away.

Nicola had prepared for this decision by buying a little wooden box with a lock. She wrote a letter expressing all the anger and uncertainty that she associated with her care home memories, and all the insight that she had discovered in our sessions. Then she locked it away in the box. Every time she thought about the care home after that point, she remembered the box. She said: "I realised I didn't have to get upset anymore – I'd already said my piece and put it away".

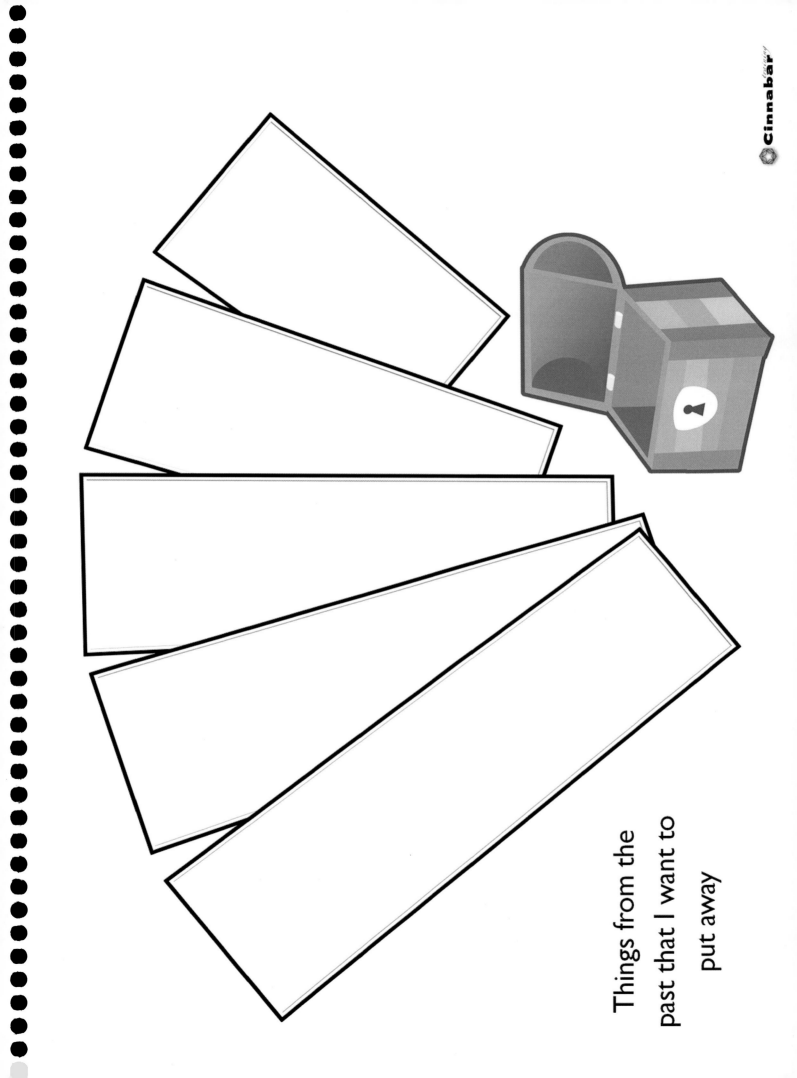

Things from the
past that I want to
put away

3.

Timeline

Every client has a history. Even the quietest of lives is made up of hundreds of events which shape who we become. Moving home, changing schools, new jobs, relationships, friendships, births, deaths and accidents all appear as milestones along the path from birth to the present day and beyond.

The Timeline enables counsellors to see the progression of these events and build a picture of the client's life. This can provide context to the issues they have brought to their sessions.

The Timeline can also be used to identify event cascades. These occur when multiple events follow each other over a relatively short space of time. The client is often unaware of the cumulative effect of a difficult series of events, harshly judging their own ability to cope. Showing them the events on paper can allow them to see just how much they dealt with at that time.

The emotional effect of a sequence of events can be quite different from that of one event alone. A bereavement, for example, can colour all the events which follow. A wedding, a birth, a new house can all become bitter sweet in the shadow of a loved one's loss. If these events all occur within a couple of years, they can also contribute to the client's stress no matter how happy or positive they are in isolation.

The Timeline can be used to explore patterns of cause and effect by looking back in time to events that are connected by geography or person or activity. For example, what was happening in your life the last time you saw your mother? Is that similar to what is happening now? What had happened to you before your new job? Has this happened before?

Timelines can take the form of a simple list of dated events in chronological order, or entries can be divided either side of a central line. For example, one side might show events relating to "being ill", with all other events entered on the other side. This arrangement can show causal patterns between the client's experiences and their health, for example if illness followed periods of stress or serious illness prompted the client to make changes in their life.

Other ways of separating events might be to identify those relating to a particular family member, those involving losses, or those involving work. Different types of event can also be signified through the use of different coloured pens, drawing around some entries, or using small stickers.

Case study: Terry was a prisoner serving a sentence for burglary. He had a long history of criminal activity beginning with petty theft when he was only 10 years old. During the first session I realised he had moved around a lot in his childhood. The disruptions had begun at an early age when his father had moved in and out of his life, each time moving the family as he pursued work. Eventually his father had left them and his mum had died and Terry had been taken into the care system. Each foster carer and group home involved packing up and moving on.

We built a timeline with moves listed on the left side. We left space in between entries, continuing onto another sheet when we ran out of room. Then we added all the times he had got into trouble on the right hand side.

Terry saw that every time he had moved, he had reacted with criminal behaviour. Over the next few sessions we talked about the losses he had experienced with each disruption. We talked about his loss of control, security and trust, about his anger as a little boy at being "pulled around", and we discovered triggers relating to these experiences that were still affecting his offending behaviour as an adult.

Cinnabar

Key events or causes

Timeline

Other events or effects

4.

What are you carrying around?

When a client becomes absorbed with a problem, frustration and anxiety can colour all their other activities and interactions. At night, they may try to put their concerns to one side but find they lie awake with their mind racing.

Stress builds as the situation continues and as new problems are added to the pile.

Clients can feel as though they carry this pile of problems on their shoulders, like a heavy burden. As more and more problems are added, the burden becomes harder to define and harder to deal with.

This tool encourages clients to picture their emotional burden as a rucksack. Within the rucksack are their numerous concerns, each in a different tin or container.

Unpacking the rucksack to reveal these individual containers helps to separate out the issues, enabling them to be discussed and explored.

Containers can hold:

- Negative emotions

- Things you regret

- People you are trying to please

- Thoughts you wish you didn't have

- Things you're worried will happen

- Memories that make you feel bad

- People who have left you

- Negative ideas you hold about yourself

Ask your client to label the containers with whatever has distracted them over the previous day or week. What has weighed heavily on them? Younger clients may like to embellish the containers with imagined or drawn-on features such as locks or secret drawers. Now explore each container and discuss strategies for handling them.

The concept can also be used in a visualisation exercise aimed at de-stressing after a busy day. Ask your client to imagine the weight of the rucksack on their back, and then to imagine taking it off and putting it away.

Case study: Jessica had just given birth to her first child. Her husband was loving but worked long hours. His mother had begun to drop in regularly to help out. Jessie came to counselling because her husband was worried; she cried every day.

When we talked about her life, she was adamant that she didn't have anything to 'fuss about' and felt guilty about being ill. It became apparent that she was holding herself to very high standards.

We used the rucksack to map out the various weights she was carrying around. These included "breastfeeding pressure", "best friend is a super mum", "making my husband proud", "not messing up as a mum", "pressure from mother-in-law".

We talked about how normal it was for her to feel the weight of each of her issues, and how together they had become a burden that was affecting her ability to function. Most of all, we talked about how any person would need to put some of these weights down in order to stay healthy. Jessica started to understand that it was OK to need help.

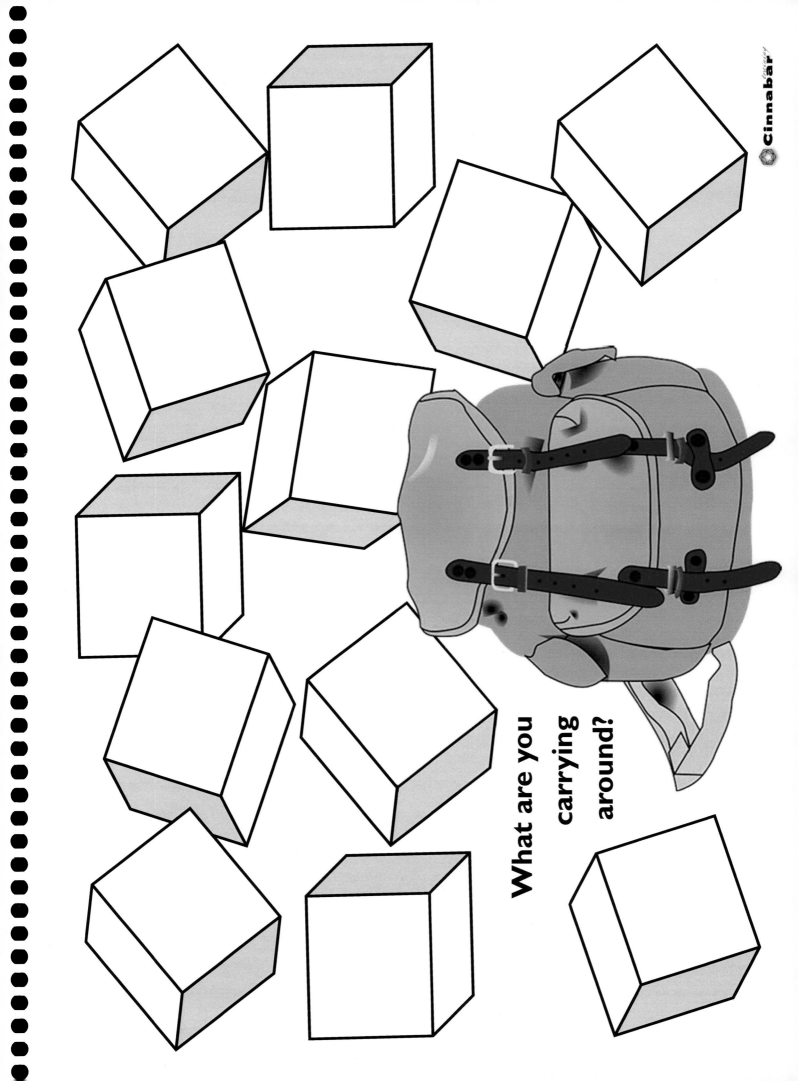

What are you carrying around?

Cinnabar

5.

Letting stress out

When using this tool, the counsellor asks the client to think of their body as though it were a bottle of fizzy drink and to imagine that each bubble inside the bottle is an emotion, or worry or concern.

As they walk around experiencing the world and its stresses, they shake up and agitate those bubbles, building the pressure up and up.

Perhaps your client is experiencing outbursts of emotion – anger, irritation, grief, frustration? Ask them to think about what happens when a bottle of fizzy drink is shaken and then opened.

Then ask them to imagine carefully opening the bottle just enough to let one bubble out at a time.

This tool can be used to plant this image in your client's mind so they can visualise releasing their stress and you can help them to address their issues in a calmer, controlled way. One bubble at a time.

Each bubble might be a person they are angry at, or something that happened that is still causing pain. They may represent multiple losses that have been building up for many years. This can be especially useful in bereavement work, where bubbles might represent "not saying goodbye", "feeling angry" or "they let me down".

Describing the fizzy bottle metaphor can sometimes be enough to provide clients with a hook that they can use to visualise and release their stress.

Or the client can work on the sheet, labelling the bubbles with each issue that concerns them. This brings the issues into the concrete world and out of the mind of the client. The sheet can then act as a focus or prompt for topics to cover in future sessions.

After identifying the bubbles that are trapped inside, younger clients sometimes like to take a practical approach to letting them out. Get a bubble blowing kit and encourage your client to imagine their stressful feelings being pushed out of their body and into each bubble with every breath. Each bubble then floats away to eventually burst.

Case study: Tom came to counselling because he had been having trouble holding his temper both at work and at home.

He identified three bubbles that were floating in his day to day life: "my car is off the road"; "new boss at work doesn't like me"; "payment is due on the new sofa".

And then he began describing bubbles that were still in the bottle because he didn't feel he could let them out without "freaking out". They were: "I owe my best mate a lot of money"; "my mum fell down because the carer was late"; "my wife kissed a guy she works with".

In each case, these bubbles referred to something that he was holding inside, and which made him feel upset. Together they produced a sense of pressure that exploded outward and caused his temper outbursts. Understanding the fizzy metaphor helped Tom to appreciate the importance of managing his emotions and not 'bottling them up'.

We talked through each bubble in turn and worked out strategies to help Tom address each one so it could be safely 'let out'. Once that pressure had been relieved, Tom felt able to talk about his underlying feelings of responsibility and inadequacy and how this related to his relationship with his dad.

We used the fizzy bottle metaphor from time to time throughout his counselling to discuss new bubbles in his life.

Cinnabar

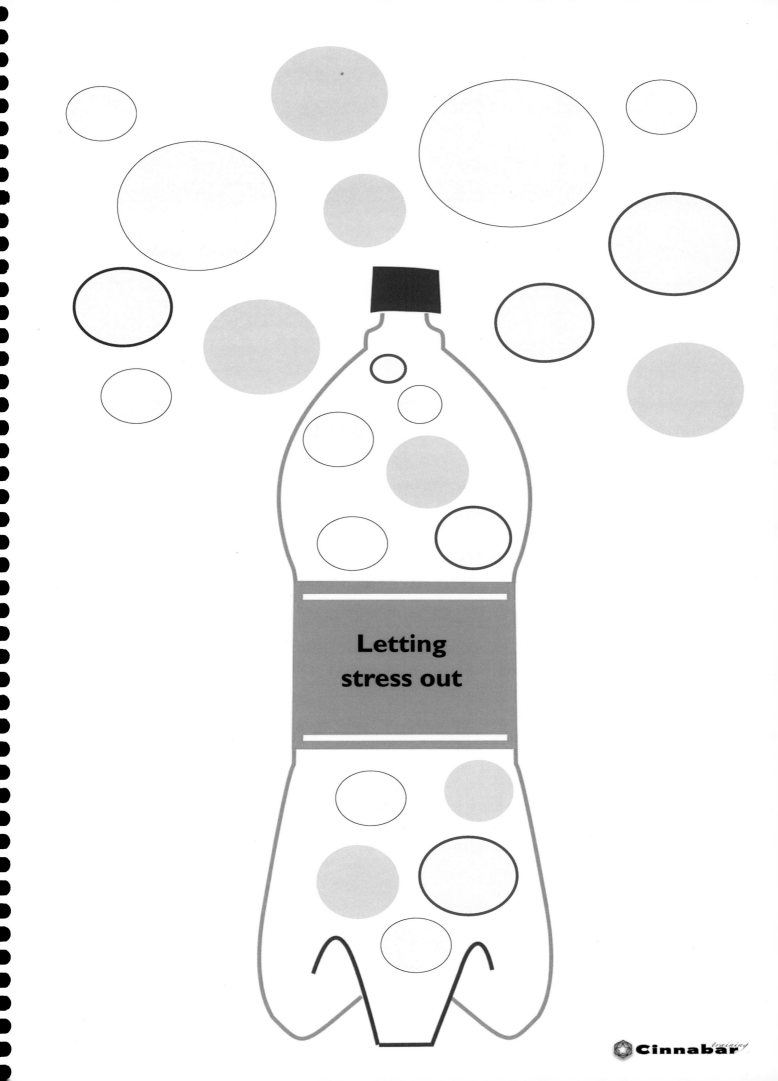

Letting
stress out

Cinnabar

6.

How I feel when...

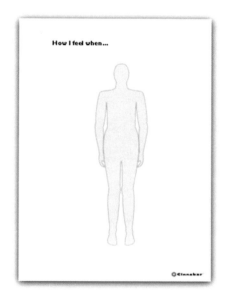

Everyday life involves many possible stressors. We are not passive bystanders when we encounter these. While our emotions are washing over us, and our thoughts are racing, our bodies are also sending us signals, ranging from the embarrassing to the uncomfortable or even painful.

These physical effects can heighten emotions and encourage distorted thinking, leading to a spiralling response.

Counsellors can try to find out what is driving this response by exploring its triggers and its origins in the past. This work can take many sessions, so an effective two-pronged approach will also explore the physical symptoms experienced by the client in order to enable them to begin retraining their body to respond in a less overwhelming way. This might reduce the impact of panic attacks, for example, by providing enough breathing room for the client to implement CBT strategies or work through insights from their sessions.

Label the top of the tool with the particular situation that is being discussed. Be as detailed as possible and include the date. Then ask your client to draw in their symptoms on the appropriate part of the body image. Use colours (e.g., colour the hands in red to indicate "hot hands") and symbols or lines (e.g., a lightning bolt going into the head to represent a "stabbing headache"). Write in labels or a key. Add numbers next to each symptom to indicate the strength of the feeling (e.g. 2 out of 5).

Discuss each symptom in turn. Work on strategies for detecting them early. Can your client do anything to feel better? (for example, running their hands under a cold tap, making sure they rest, keeping a drink in their bag).

Redo the tool regularly. Have the symptoms changed? Are they weaker? Link this tool to other journals or diaries.

This tool can also be used to monitor the side effects of drugs, or distinguish those effects from other physical responses. Label the sheet with details of current drug dosages and redo to see if the side effects reduce over time.

Case study: Helen suffered a panic attack at her father's funeral. Afterwards she reacted with stress symptoms whenever she found herself surrounded by people. It happened when she walked through her local market, when out with friends in a club, and when riding on the lift in her office building.

We chose one example – walking through the market the previous Friday on her way home from work. She drew green spirals inside the tummy area and wrote 'swirly swirly' around the outline. She coloured the face bright red with wavy heat lines coming out of the top of the head. Helen added green sweat patches under the arms. Then she coloured the fingers in black, writing 'numb' beside each hand.

We began by working on relaxation techniques Helen could use to prepare herself for expected situations as well as strategies she could use to minimise her physical reactions, such as sucking a mint or listening to music on her headphones. As we discussed variations of her response and different triggering situations, we realised that the first symptom was always the 'swirly' tummy.

We explored the origin of this symptom. The first time she remembered having this reaction was when she was 5 and had wandered away from her parents into a crowd, becoming lost and overwhelmed. Linking this to her emotional state at her father's funeral provided a lightbulb moment.

Cinnabar

How I feel when...

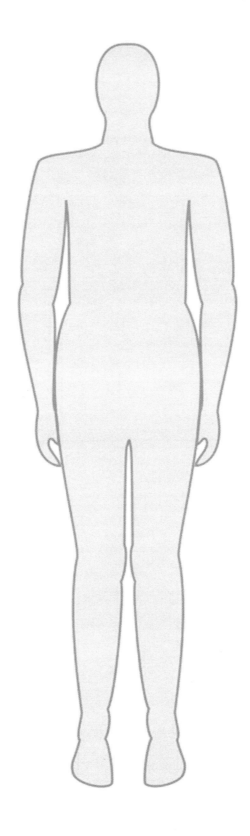

7.

Anchors

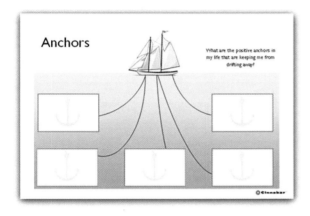

When clients explore their past, they can feel as though they have been set adrift from themselves.

Their lives become insubstantial as the past comes to life and seems more solid than the present.

Before starting this kind of exploration, establish some anchors that can ground your client when they feel vulnerable.

Anchors are people, places, goals, achievements or even affirmations that remind your client of the present world and their motivations for seeking change. They should inspire positive feelings such as pride, purpose, hope and love.

Fill in the boxes on the tool with anchors such as:

- Family or friends, for example "my new grand-daughter"

- Places or things that give pleasure, for example "imagine sitting in my garden – my sanctuary"

- Ideas about the future, for example "next year, a trip to Australia"

- Achievements, for example "I was promoted at work because I'm really good at my job"

- Affirmations or phrases, even lines of poetry that mean something to the client and strengthen their resolve, for example "this too shall pass"

Clients can keep the completed tool on their fridge or a noticeboard at home, or cut out the boxes and put them in their purse or wallet.

Some clients might like to expand on the idea and include pictures or physical representations of their anchors.

Encourage your client to revisit their anchors regularly, particularly after difficult sessions.

Case study: Louise came to counselling to explore unpleasant aspects of her childhood that had come to light after the death of her mother.

She identified three anchors on the tool before we began: "seeing my daughter get married next year", "holiday with my husband", and "my painting".

Louise began to put things relating to her daughter's wedding into a shoe box at home. This included ideas for her outfit and letters and photographs from her daughter.

She set up a countdown showing days until her holiday and put this on her fridge at home.

Finally, she took a picture of the painting she was most proud of and reduced it until it was small enough to fit in her purse.

At the end of our sessions, we spent a few minutes catching up on each anchor. Each of them reminded her that she had achievements and joys in her life. They brought her back to a positive and hopeful present after difficult sessions spent in the past.

Anchors

What are the positive anchors in my life that are keeping me from drifting away?

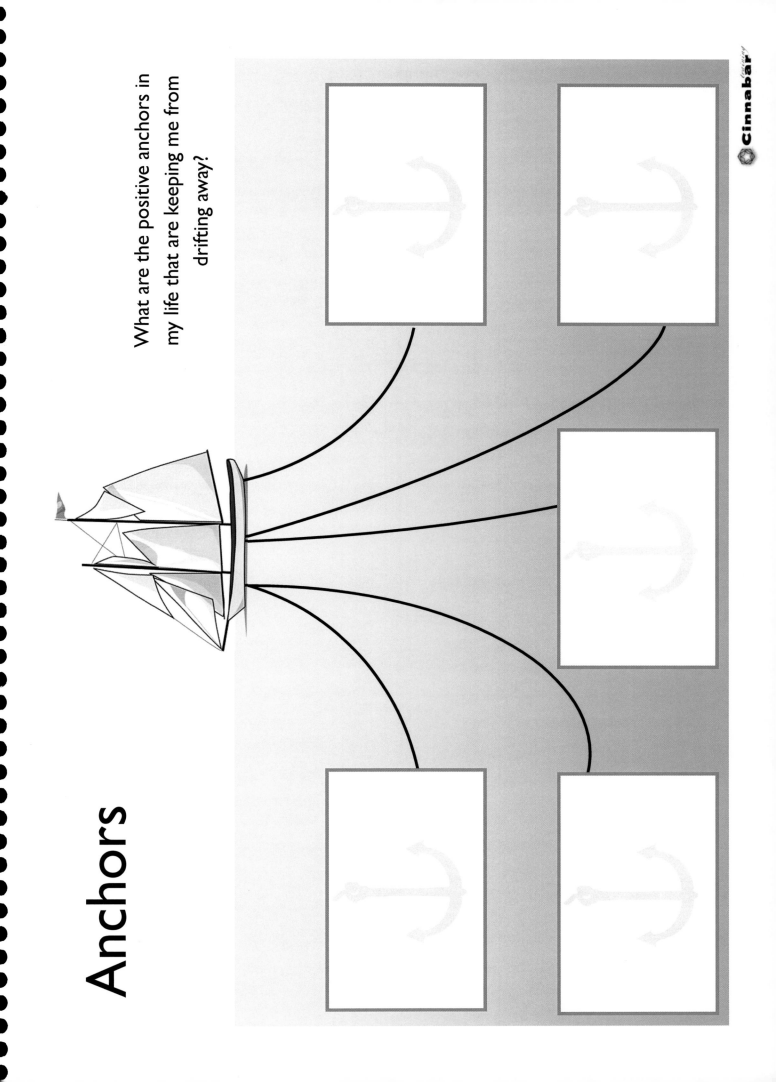

8.

Where are the people in my life?

When a client comes to counselling they can feel like they are all alone. They can sometimes see the people around them as responsibilities or problems, or even strangers. Re-connecting to the people in their life can be a positive milestone for them. Sometimes this is the reason they came to counselling, and sometimes an improvement in their relationships is a happy side-effect.

If therapy is likely to involve revisiting past trauma, it is important to discuss the client's relationships at an early stage to establish potential sources of support. This support might be from family members who would provide practical help or maybe a friend who would be available to chat over a cup of tea.

Use this tool to map out the people in your client's life, identify sources of support, or explore their relationships.

Ask your client to draw markers to indicate each of the people in their life. Markers should be positioned on the circles according to the client's perceptions, moving out from the central point to indicate a decreasing relationship. Clients may begin by using physical markers such as pebbles or shells or little toys to consider where the markers should be placed in relation to each other.

Use the exercise to prompt a discussion of the people involved, particularly the reasoning behind their relative positions on the circles. Encourage them to return to the tool if they want to update it during future sessions.

The tool can be used to describe many aspects of relationships including:

- Levels of support (place the most supportive people in the central circles)

- Closeness or trust (place those they trust the most or are closest to nearer the centre)

- Involvement in the client's life (place those they see the most in the central circles)

- Association with the past (place those who are strong triggers to past traumas in the central circles)

- Changes in relationships over time (draw two markers for each relationship – then and now – and connect them with a line)

Case study: I used this tool with Amanda to explore her relationships. She felt alone and adrift despite having friends and family living nearby.

I asked her to choose coloured stones to represent her family and then to arrange these on the tool around the central "Me" point. We talked about her reasoning – Why had she put her friend there? Why was her mum further out than her brother?

We discovered that, for Amanda, closeness was linked to acceptance. People who were close to her were less likely to question her decisions. Those who had disapproved of her life choices had been sent to the outer circles.

Over the next few sessions we explored the roots of her need for unquestioning acceptance and worked on ways she could reconnect with her family and long-term friends.

Cinnabar

Where are the people in my life?

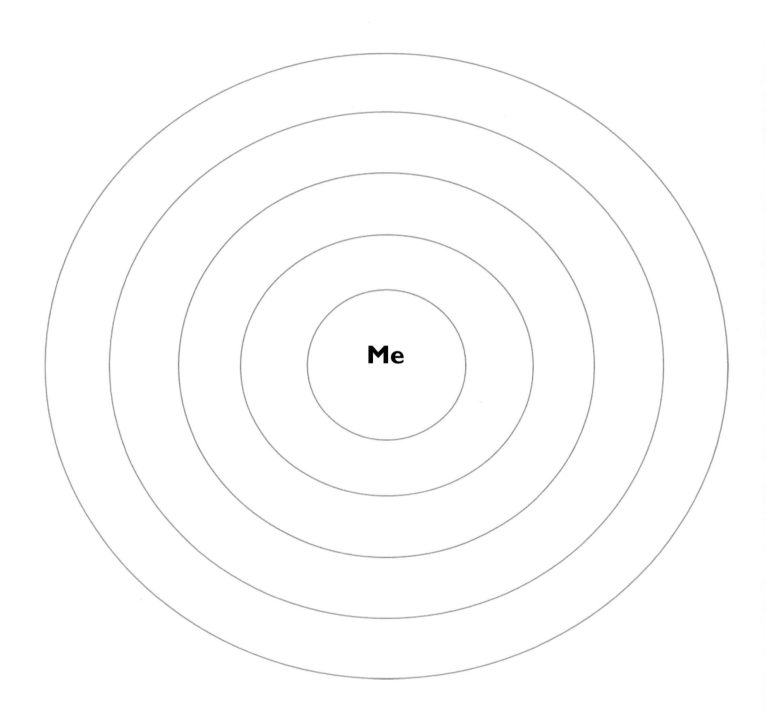

Me

9.

Me and me

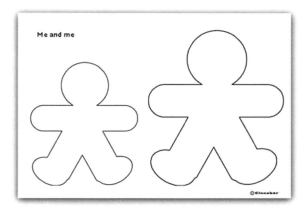

We all change over time.

The differences are usually gradual and it can be surprising to realise how the years and events have had their impact.

Some of these changes will come from positive growth as we age and experience the milestones of a well-lived life. This may involve developing qualities such as patience, perseverance, humour and tolerance.

Some of these changes will come from our reaction to the negative experiences in our lives. Trauma, abuse, loss and betrayal can affect our personality, encouraging negative traits to develop such as distrust, obsession, intolerance and bitterness.

Looking forward, we also project an image of our preferred future self. Sometimes this involves identifying aspects of our identity that we hope will one day fade through our self-work, and sometimes it's about aspects of our identity that we are proud of and resolve to keep.

This tool can be used in a variety of ways. It can provide a concrete undertaking to clients who are wanting to make changes, or provide a reminder for those who need to remember how far they have come. It can also be used to separate and describe different roles or contexts such as parent or worker. In each case it can be used to open a conversation about change and the causal influences in the client's life.

Label each gingerbread person and then fill them with words, drawings and ideas. Gingerbread people may represent:

- "me now" and "me then"

- "the me I want to take with me" and "the me I want to leave behind"

- "me now" and "the me I'd like to be"

- "me at work" and "me at home"

- "me as dad" and "me as son"

- "me when I'm afraid" and "me when I'm not afraid"

Case study: Claire came to counselling through an Employee Assistance Programme. She was stressed and disillusioned with her job, despite working at a very senior level in her company. She felt that she had lost touch with the ideals she had had as a younger woman, so we used *Me and me* to explore what she had wanted for herself back then.

She labelled the larger gingerbread person: "the dreamer" to indicate who she was at 20 years old, just starting her first full time job. Words to describe how "the dreamer" felt about her future career included: "helping people", "being brave", "something artsy", "not being bored", and "time to play".

She labelled the smaller gingerbread person: "stuck and sad". She added words like: "desk all day", "isolated", "always the bad guy", "on call at the weekend", "do as I'm told".

We discussed the route her career had taken, and the reasons at each point that she had moved away from her aspirations. She realised that most of her decisions had been made in reaction to events in her life – getting married, moving house, having children.

We talked about positive influences in her life and positive aspects of the woman she had become. We also talked about the opportunity she now had to be proactive, and the changes that she could make at work.

Me and me

10.

What's beneath your anger?

The word "anger" can mean different things to different people.

To some it conjures up scenes of parents arguing, maybe something being thrown. To others it is referenced by the memory of standing in the playground with fists clenched. Still others may identify it as the hot leaden ball in their stomach that makes their heart race.

To make things even more complicated, anger is also an iceberg emotion. This means that there is more going on beneath the surface that we can't see.

This tool is about exploring the individual's experience of anger – establishing a shared vocabulary between the client and the counsellor – and also identifying the other feelings that are beneath or behind the client's anger.

If a client has difficulties with their anger, ask them to think of a specific time they were angry. Ask them to pick out two or three words from the tool that might describe how their anger felt that time. What do these words mean to them? What does this reveal?

Is their anger always made of that same combination of feelings?

Words are like keys into our memories and feelings. Just the sight of some words can make us feel something. And what your client feels when they think of a word will often be very personal and unique to their history.

Pick one of the words they have chosen and ask them to think back to the very first time they think they remember feeling that way. Explore the memory and be on the lookout for similar elements to those that accompany your client's anger in the present.

Case study: Steve had a tendency to get involved in fights. This had landed him in prison more than once and he was determined it wouldn't happen again. However, he was proud of his ability to handle himself and unable to see how he would ever feel able to walk away from a conflict.

The first word he chose on the tool was "protect". We talked about how he felt compelled to get involved even if it had nothing to do with him, because he had to stand up for others. He thought about the first time he had ever felt protective in a fight, and this led to a discussion of his experiences in the care system and the rules of friendship that he had absorbed.

I asked Steve to return to the words, and to think again about how he feels in the present when he is angry and ready for a fight. The next word was "lonely" followed quickly by "vanished".

All three words together unlocked a memory of feeling left behind as other children left the foster care arrangement and he remained. The friendships he had begun were cut off with hardly any notice and he developed a deep well of anger toward adults and authority figures.

Steve realised that in all his fighting there was usually someone he identified as the 'underdog' and that his need to protect them was the result of the emotional losses he had never properly expressed.

What's beneath your anger?

afraid ashamed lost vulnerable absent

insecure overwhelmed humiliated helpless

trapped right bewildered frightened humbled

small degraded tired stunned anxious slow

troubled embarrassed nervous worried

vanished concerned tense uneasy satisfied

edgy unappreciated disappointed frustrated

powerful manipulated puzzled disturbed

mystified upset under pressure insulted

stressed exhausted panicky lonely confused

protect muddled jittery injured strong

11.

Who has the power?

Survivors of abuse often feel that what was done to them was their own fault.

By identifying with the small child in this picture many survivors of abuse are able to understand in a very simple way that the abuser had all of the power. It could not have been their fault. They were small, and the abuser had all the power.

Simply show this tool to your client. You might ask them: how could the little child in this picture possibly stand up to the adult? Often, words are not necessary.

Allow the client to decide for themselves who the adult figure represents. This may include not only those who have hurt them but also those who remind them of that hurt. People who remind them of past abusers may continue to trigger difficult reactions in the present. Reducing the abuser to a cardboard cut-out or silhouette enables similarities to be identified.

The child image used in this tool is that of a very young boy or girl. If your client was abused as an older child or as an adult, they can usually still relate to the image. The key is in the *difference* between the two figures and how this difference relates to power and control; vulnerability makes us feel small, even if we are not small.

If desired, a similar effect can be achieved by asking the client to draw stick figures to the approximate proportions.

This is one of the most powerful tools in this collection. It can elicit strong emotions and should be used carefully.

Consider the best time to use it, when you are sure that your client can deal with the emotions it will release. Make sure you allow enough time in the session to bring your client back down from the initial outpouring of emotion.

Once the idea of blame is lifted, there can be a euphoric reaction as new possibilities for the future present themselves, or there can be some depression as clients are forced to change their understanding of themselves and those who were involved in their abuse. Encourage them not to make any drastic decisions before the next session.

Case study: Robert was 40 years old. When he was eight years old he was molested by his uncle at a family wedding. He had never told anyone. Since then he had attended many family events where he had seen his abuser. After each of these, he plunged into weeks of depression. When I asked him why he didn't tell his mother, he said it wasn't that simple. He said: "I was pretty wild as a kid" and "I have to take responsibility for what happened too."

I silently showed him the picture. He looked at it for three or four minutes without saying anything, then abruptly began to cry. "I'd never thought of it like that," he said.

I supported him in that moment by simply sitting quietly while he worked through the emotions that were flooding through him. After a while, we began to talk about how he was feeling.

In the following sessions we talked about the concepts of consent and responsibility that he had absorbed as a little boy, and the implications of his new perspective for his relationships with the rest of the family.

⬡ Cinnabar

Who has the power?

12.

Blame & Fault

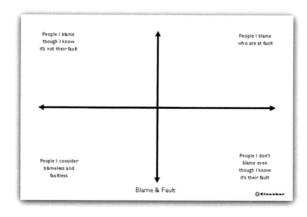

When things happen, people usually feel compelled to identify patterns of cause and effect, fault and innocence.

Something like a car accident on an empty road may involve the contributions of a diverse cast of characters such as the person who was driving, their passengers, the people they had just spent time with, the mechanic who last checked the car, and even the person who cut the hedges beside that patch of road.

Events involving mistreatment or abuse may involve an even more diverse cast ranging from family and friends, to people from social services, police, doctors, and school teachers.

Being human, our consideration of the relative contribution each of these people made to the event is flawed. Fault should be assigned to those who are responsible for that particular mistake or offense, and yet we frequently assign it to the wrong person or refuse to acknowledge the part played by the actual culprit. Blame should be assigned to the same people who are at fault, but we often blame those who had nothing to do with the situation simply because they have angered us for some other reason.

Use this tool to explore a client's perceptions of the people around them. Choose an event in your client's life. Ask your client to draw markers at the appropriate places on the chart to indicate their perceptions of those involved. When they have entered all possible participants, discuss each category in turn.

Questions might include:

- How accurate are you? What factors are affecting the picture?

- Has anyone moved position since it happened? Would you like someone to move position?

- Why do you blame x if you know it's not their fault? How is this manifesting itself in your behaviour toward them?

- How are you expressing your blame of those who are at fault? Is this healthy for you?

- What role is being played by those you consider blameless and faultless? Are they observing the situation or participating in it? Are they contributing an opinion?

- Why aren't you expressing blame toward x when you know they are at fault?

This tool can also be used with stones or buttons which can be moved around. Label them or use different colours to identify people involved.

Case study: Jane and Ben lost their 13 year old son in a drugs-related death two years ago. They came to counselling to try and rebuild their relationship and resolve recurring arguments.

They each filled in a blame chart for us to discuss in their sessions. We found areas of agreement for them to build on, and areas of disagreement that could be explored in a safe environment.

In particular, Ben had placed himself on his chart in the area for "People I blame who are at fault" whereas Jane had put him in her chart in "People I blame though I know it's not their fault". The realisation that Jane did not really believe Ben was at fault helped Ben a great deal.

Further discussions included the role of their son's friends (and parental decisions that had been made regarding these friends), support from extended family, and the opinions of well-meaning friends (at the time and since).

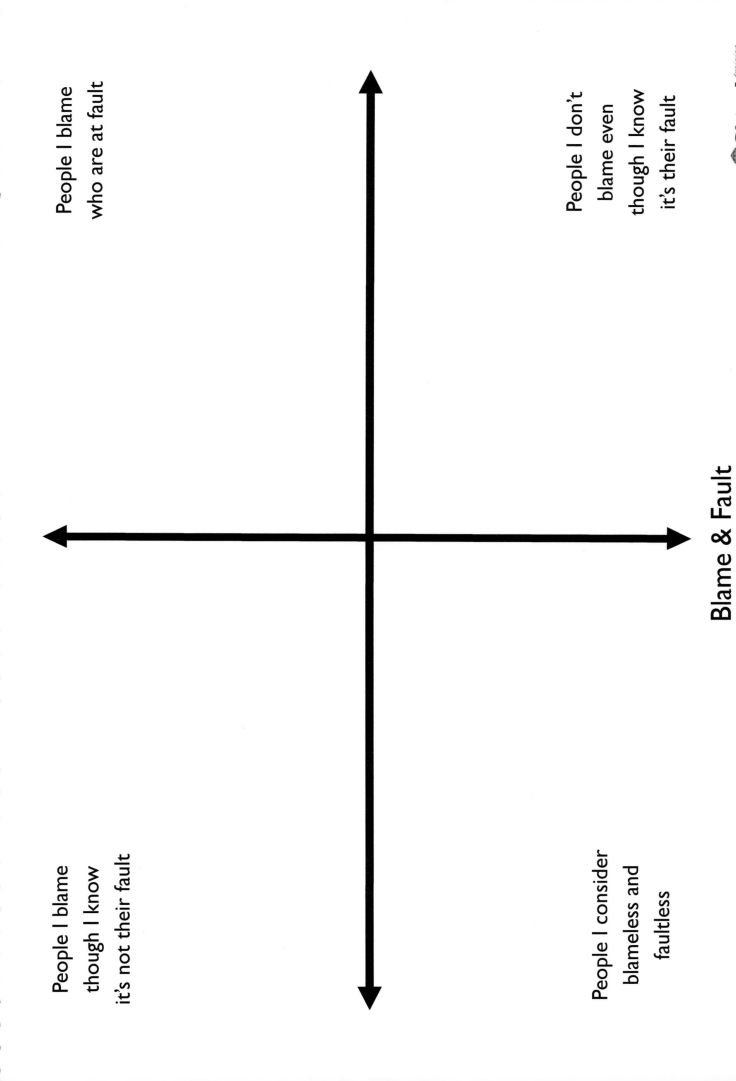

People I blame
who are at fault

People I don't
blame even
though I know
it's their fault

People I blame
though I know
it's not their fault

People I consider
blameless and
faultless

Blame & Fault

Cinnabar

13.

Child parent, Adult parent

When clients revisit their childhood during counselling, they inevitably encounter the memory of their parents.

These are the parents from the past – as seen through child eyes and the distance of many years.

Sometimes these parents were abusive.

Sometimes they were neglectful or unavailable.

Sometimes they were loving and well-meaning, but also powerless and unaware that bad things were happening to their child.

Clients can find it hard to talk about these 'child parents', especially if they have developed a new relationship as adults with their mum and dad. The 'adult parents' are now old and possibly frail, and they are often completely different in personality and motivation.

No matter how badly they were treated in their childhood, it can sometimes seem to clients that memories of their parents in the past are best left undisturbed. "Speaking badly" of their parent feels wrong and releases emotions that are carried into present day family visits and relationships with extended family.

Clients can feel that acknowledging their parents' failings from the past would mean betraying their parents in the present.

This tool is a great way to give your clients permission to explore how they felt toward their parents in the past by clearly separating the 'child parents' from the 'adult parents'.

Ask your client to describe their parents now. Put these words around the bottom picture – the adult parents. Include their personality, things they like, and strong associations. Tell your client that these are the parents of today, and it is ok to love these parents and respect them.

Then ask them to describe their child parents and put these words around the top picture. Tell your client that it is ok to feel all kinds of feelings towards these parents – talking about these feelings cannot cross the line to affect their relationship with their adult parents.

Case study: Emma came to counselling because she felt untethered. Since leaving home she hadn't stayed in a job or relationship for longer than two years. It soon became clear that she was reacting to unresolved emotions from her childhood when her mother had been an abusive alcoholic.

Emma was now a part time carer to her mum, and spent many hours with her. She described their friendship, and the wonderful things her mum had done for her including paying off one of her loans. During our sessions Emma rationalised her mother's past drinking behaviour, and was uncomfortable accessing her negative memories from that time.

We used the child parent/ adult parent tool. Emma wrote about her adult mum first: "soft hands", "jasmine smell", "crosswords and tea", "telling her about my day", "hugs". Then we talked about her child mum and she wrote: "finding her unconscious", "smelly", "no dinner", "angry all the time", "tells me it's my fault", "can't have friends round".

By drawing a mental line between the two, Emma was able to explore her feelings of rootlessness and how they related to the chaotic mum of her childhood without damaging her relationship with the nurturing mum she knew now.

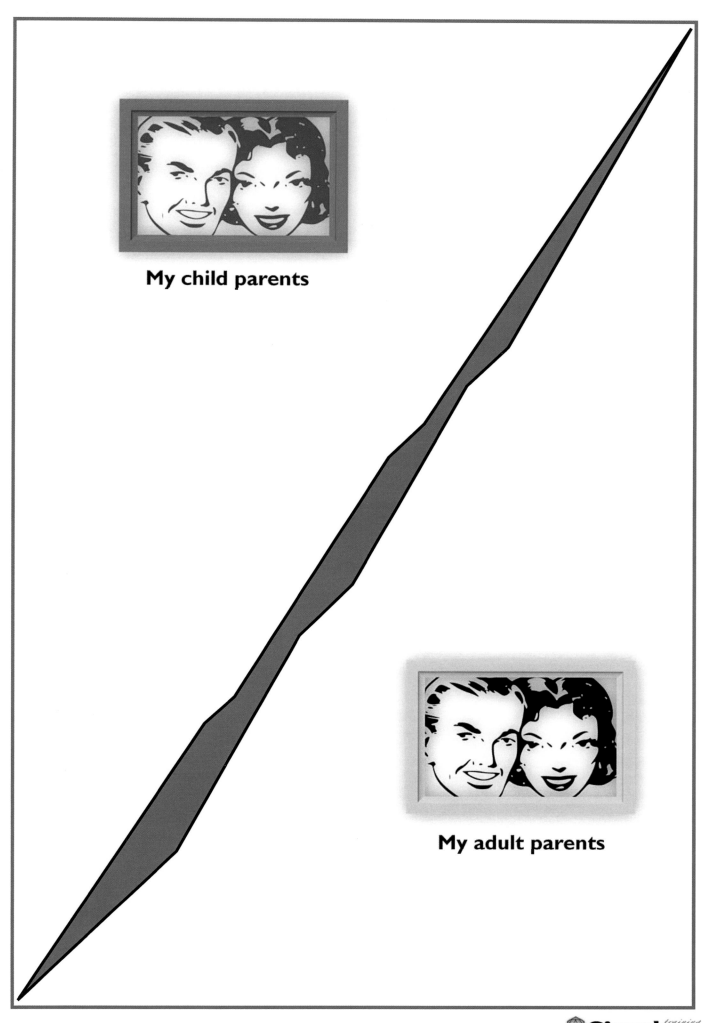

My child parents

My adult parents

Cinnabar training

14.

Changing Relationships

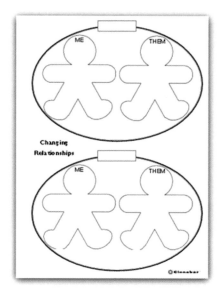

Spouses, children, parents, co-workers, bosses, employees, friends, neighbours, club members, dog walkers…. We encounter people every day.

Sometimes our contact with others is fleeting, based on passing through a shared context. Other times our relationships emerge after intimate experience and years of history.

Some relationships can provoke powerful emotions, such as those felt between a bully and their victim, while other relationships can feel distant and unconnected, such as family members that share only Christmas and birthday cards.

Relationships also change over time, as the people in them change. This can be a slow, gradual process or a sudden shift in connection as a result of an experience or event in our lives. And sometimes we look at our relationships and want to bring about a change for ourselves – to review where we are now and plan a way forward to where we want to be.

Use this tool to explore relationships and the people in them over time.

Ask your client to label one of the gingerbread people in the top bubble on the tool and to describe their own roles and personality in this particular relationship, for example, "the funny one" or "always in charge". Then label the other figure with words to describe the other person in this relationship in a similar fashion, for example, "the clever one" or "easy-going".

In the space inside the bubble, ask your client to write down how they interact and who they are together, for example "the perfect couple" or "argue about nothing" or "don't go out anymore".

Then ask your client to describe the relationship they would like to have in the second bubble. Alternatively, start by describing the relationship "now" in the first bubble and then move back in time to explore how they used to be "before" in the second bubble. In each case, consider the questions: Who am I to them? Who are they to me? Who are we together?

Some relationships have different faces in different contexts. Use the tool to explore "us in private" and "us in public", for example.

Case study: Hazel had a 15 year old daughter who was experimenting with alcohol, drugs and boys. The atmosphere at home had deteriorated to the point where mum and daughter were barely speaking, and single mum Hazel was feeling stressed and tearful most of the time.

We started with a bubble labelled "us now" to describe what was currently happening between them. Words inside her gingerbread person included "afraid to speak" and "not in control". Inside the other figure Hazel wrote words like "cold" and "stranger" and "manipulative". In the space between: "notes on fridge" and "sighing" and "no physical contact".

We shifted to the second bubble ("us before") and explored their relationship from two years ago. Hazel's daughter had been "fun to spend time with" and Hazel had felt "trusted" and "listened to". Together there had been "laughter" and "girl nights" and "lots of hugs".

Hazel and I started a fresh tool and repeated the exercise looking at Hazel's experience as a teenager and her changing relationship with her own mum. Hazel had undergone a similar "pulling away" process at that age and had had similar fall outs with her mum. By looking into her own past, Hazel found that her anger toward her daughter greatly reduced and she was able to draw reassurance from the subsequent relationship she had forged with her mum as an adult.

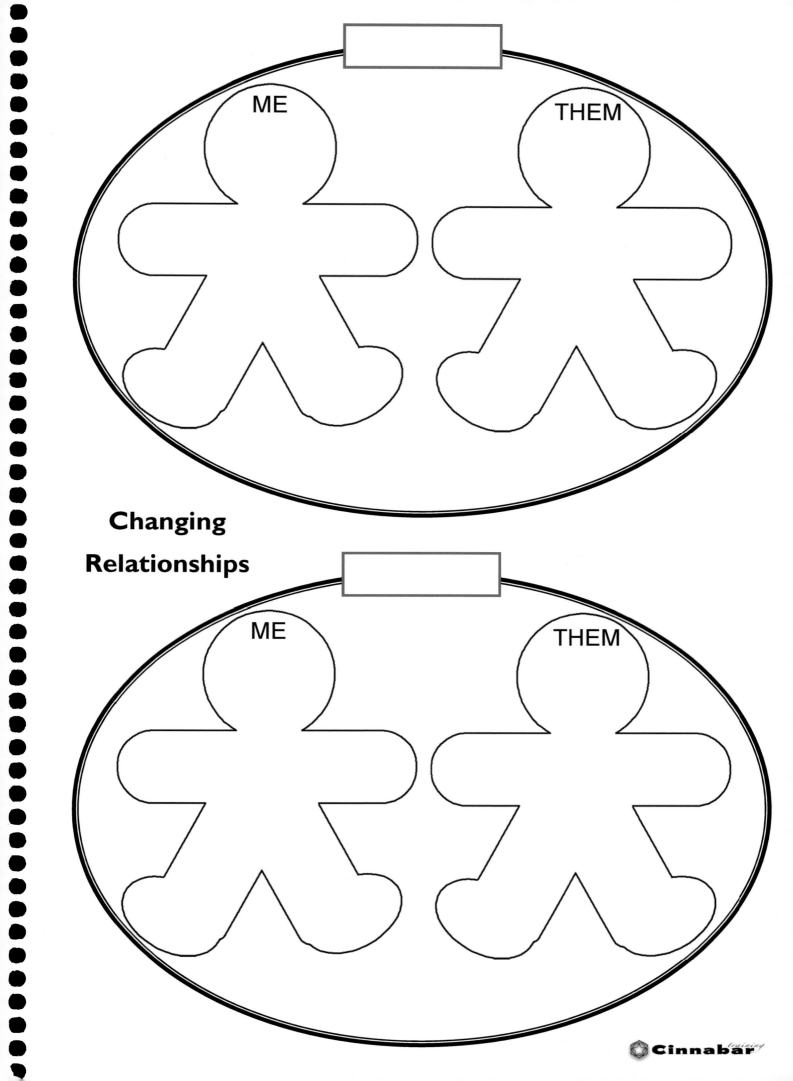

ME THEM

Changing

Relationships

ME THEM

15.

Moving on from my regret

Throughout life, people lose things – tangible things like people and objects, but also intangible things like opportunities and potential. Sometimes we believe that we had a measure of control over these losses and this can lead to feelings of disappointment or regret about things we think we should have done, or shouldn't have done at some crucial point in our past.

Regrets can have a powerful effect on clients, hijacking their reactions to future events and decisions, and painting them with strong negative emotions. Talking therapies can explore these feelings and try to identify reasons for them; however, after this process, it can be useful to look ahead and identify ways of moving on.

To do this, focus on the present: first of all, what are their feelings now about what happened then? And second of all: how can they move on from those feelings? This tool offers a way to generate positive ideas to move on.

First, ask your client to identify a regret and write it in the large square at the centre of the tool. They might focus on specific events such as "I regret fighting with dad last Christmas", or it might be more general such as "my career path isn't what I wanted".

Then – skipping the 'my first step' box for now – work with them to fill in the bubbles all around the page with ideas about how they might move away from the way their regret makes them feel.

Ideas might be about making practical changes to the patterns of behaviour that they have been stuck in since the regret first occurred, for example "start seeing dad on Sundays again", "pick one old photo to display" or "make amends to x". Or the ideas might be about making emotional changes to the feelings that grew from the regret, for example "decide to be kinder to myself". There might be ideas for one action ("get another qualification") or for a series of actions ("start recording what I eat every day").

Then, go back to the 'my first step' box. In here, ask your client to write one small practical step that they can take to begin their journey. For example, this first step might be to "send my cv to a recruitment agency".

Each completed step should be seen as an achievement, moving the client away from the negative emotions and memories associated with their regret.

Case study: Tina had recently separated from her second husband after 25 years of marriage with no children. It had been an unhappy marriage, ending when she discovered him in bed with his long-term mistress. She said she could trace everything that was wrong in her life to her decision to marry him. Her regret affected her mood and attitude toward the future, making her sad and angry and hesitant about opening up to anyone or anything new. She felt it was "too late".

We used the regret tool, starting with "I regret marrying Joe" in the centre. We talked about how she felt when she thought about her regret, and what she wished she could change.

Her ideas included: "make a list of good things that happened in those years (start with learning how to drive)", "get back in touch with old friends", "go to dance class", "start treating myself like someone special", "forgive myself", "start a new hobby", "book a holiday", "think about 3 things to be grateful for before bed each night". Her first step was to "book an appointment to get a haircut and colour" before our next session.

Moving on from my regret

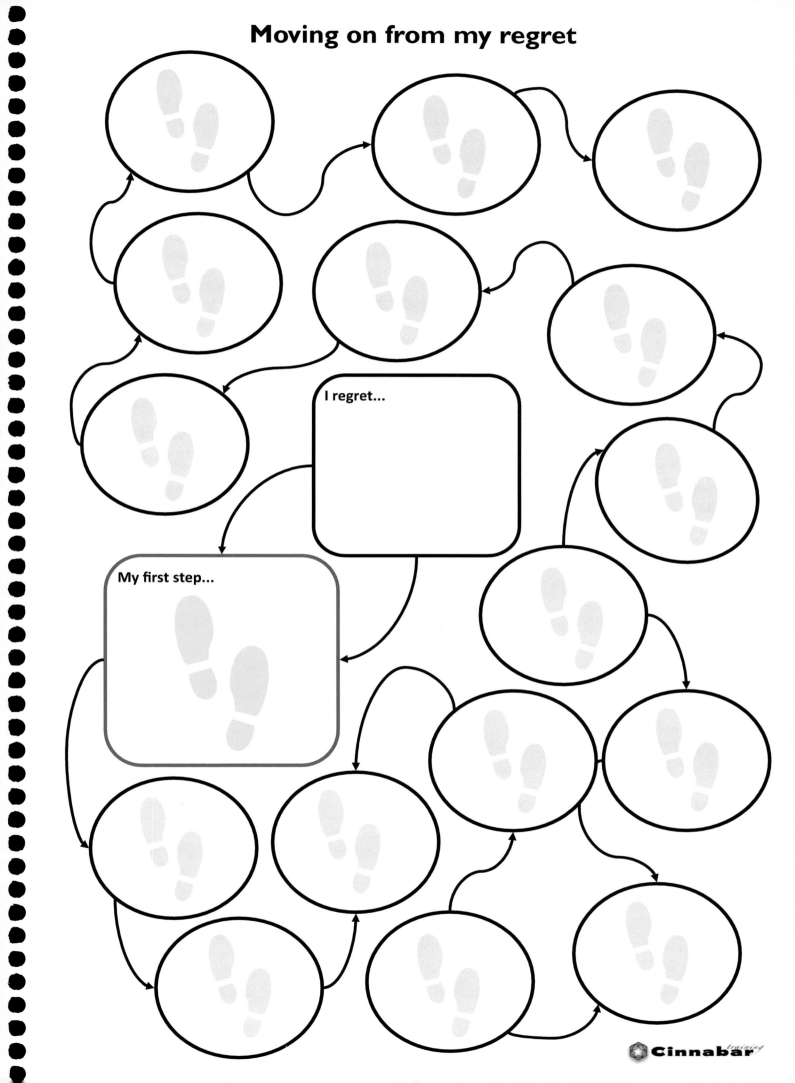

I regret...

My first step...

Cinnabar *training*

16.

I'm giving up...

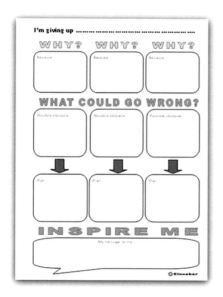

Whether its smoking or alcohol, sugar or swearing, when you're trying to give something up it helps to have a plan.

This is especially true when we try to do something difficult such as giving up a behaviour that we have come to depend on (e.g. smoking that all important cigarette at lunch to help us cope with a job that we hate).

Many times we fail in our attempt to give up something in our lives because we lose sight of our reasons for our decision. Perhaps it becomes a test of our willpower or part of a deal we make with a family member, and we forget about the health fears that first prompted the decision to quit.

Sometimes we turn a corner only to find ourselves surprised by a temptation or trigger point that we don't know how to react to without slipping back into comforting habits. This might be a sudden loss or setback at work, or something as simple as a friend's birthday party or anniversary meal.

We might try to exercise our willpower, but this is usually easy prey to distraction, tiredness or social pressure.

This tool will guide your client in the creation of a solid plan.

It will give your client a concrete reminder of their reasons – why they've decided that their life will be better without the thing they're trying to quit

– and it will help them to anticipate the hurdles they might encounter along the way and set out some tactics for dealing with them.

At the bottom of the tool there is also a box for clients to add inspiring quotes or messages to themselves. This can be added to over time.

Case study: Alice was single and successful at work. She came to counselling because she was spending £50 every week gambling on scratch cards. We worked on identifying the issues which drove her behaviour, including her fear of losing her job and her volatile relationship with her mother.

Alongside this work, Alice used the tool to draw up a plan for giving up her gambling behaviour.

In the "Because Boxes" she wrote: "I want to spend the money on clothes and pretty things for me instead"; "I always feel so depressed and stupid after I lose"; and "I know from experience that winning doesn't make me feel good for more than a few seconds".

She identified two main obstacles that she could anticipate and plan for:

"I go into the corner shop to buy groceries (and see all the scratch cards by the till)" could be offset by the following planned responses: "use the supermarket nearby instead and avoid the tobacco counter; look away from the corner shop when I walk past; walk a different route; distract myself by checking my phone as I walk past".

"My friends all do scratch cards" could be minimised as a trigger by: "don't go into the shop with friends; tell them what I'm trying to do; don't sit with them while they check their cards; don't talk about their cards".

At the bottom of the tool, Alice wrote a quote that she had seen online which she found particularly powerful: "Gambling is the sure way of getting nothing for something".

She put the tool on her fridge at home and told me that she read it every time she opened the door.

I'm giving up ....

WHY?   WHY?   WHY?

Because:	Because:	Because:

WHAT COULD GO WRONG?

Possible obstacle:	Possible obstacle:	Possible obstacle:

Plan:	Plan:	Plan:

INSPIRE ME

My message to me:

17.

Making a decision

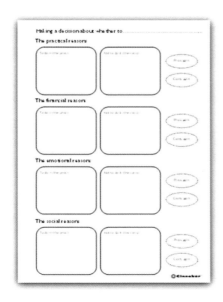

Clients often come to counselling because they are struggling with a decision.

It might be about whether to end a relationship, or whether to forgive someone. It might be about seeking a new direction, or working out how to respond to a crisis.

Many people are familiar with the idea of listing the pros and cons of a particular course of action (the points for and against). Some people favour the side with the most items listed. Others weight the different items in their lists – some reasons are larger in scope than others – then make their decisions.

This tool extends this traditional method to provide a more in depth look at the implications of a decision, particularly looking at the practical, financial, emotional and social reasons for and against a course of action. Ask your client to fill in the boxes with their reasons:

- Practical: these reasons will be about the effect of the decision on what they physically have to do. For example, having to change jobs, move home, clear out possessions, give something up.

- Financial: these reasons will be about the effect of the decision on their finances. For example, less income, increased monthly expenses, large lump sum payment needed.

- Emotional: these reasons will be about how the decision might make them feel and about feelings that they hope will disappear. They should also include the emotional implications of the decision for the people around them as this will affect the client too – e.g. the kids will be upset.

- Social: these reasons will be about how the decision might affect their relationships. For example, spending more time with a spouse, getting out and about and meeting more people

Once they have filled in all of the boxes, discuss the reasons in each group. Decide for each group which side "wins". Then consider the overall picture.

Case study: Paul worked the night shift in a warehouse. He had been referred to counselling by his GP because of stress and an increase in his drinking. He had been offered a job in another city but said he didn't know what to do. We used the tool to have a methodical look at his options.

Practical reasons: most of the reasons in this category were "against" moving away. He would have to put most of his possessions into storage, and live in a small bedsit until he was established. In the "for" box, his new job would involve working regular hours during the day.

Financial reasons: most of these were positive reasons "for" the move. Paul would get a higher salary in the new job, and wouldn't need a car.

Emotional reasons: In the "for" reasons box, Paul said that he felt excitement and hope for a new start. In the "against" box – along with a little bit of fear at moving away and starting something new – were his fears about leaving his 2 year old son behind with his ex-wife.

Social reasons: If he moved away, there was a real possibility that Paul's relationship with his son would suffer.

Paul said he felt more in control after going through all the different aspects of his decision. He realised that his relationship with his son was his main concern. We spent time linking this to his childhood experiences with his own dad and also discussed ways he could stay connected as a father if he took the job.

◯ Cinnabar

Making a decision about whether to..

The practical reasons

To do it (the pros):	Not to do it (the cons):

Pros win

Cons win

The financial reasons

To do it (the pros):	Not to do it (the cons):

Pros win

Cons win

The emotional reasons

To do it (the pros):	Not to do it (the cons):

Pros win

Cons win

The social reasons

To do it (the pros):	Not to do it (the cons):

Pros win

Cons win

18.

Creating a STRIPE goal

Goal setting can be an important part of therapy and a doorway to change. However, many goals are never achieved. This can be because they are unrealistic or vague, or simply because we run out of the motivation needed to keep moving toward them.

One way to make our goals as robust as possible is to use a framework when creating them.

The SMART goal model (Specific, Measurable, Achievable, Relevant and Timely), for example, is the framework that is currently used by many counsellors and support workers to guide the goal setting process for their clients.

However, that particular model was originally developed for the business community to use, and we believe it is not a natural fit with personal or therapeutic goal setting. So we created an alternative.

The STRIPE approach guides you through the six important features of a personal or therapeutic goal:

S – Specific – What are you focusing on? It is easier to know whether there is an improvement in your life if you aim to change something specific. Also, include a timescale in every goal. For example, instead of "improve my relationship" think about "for one month spend more time with my wife outside the house".

T – Truthful – Are you being honest? Be clear about your motives and the reality of your situation. For example, "getting a promotion at work" might be your goal, but is this something *you* want or is it something your boss is pushing you to do? Are you really ready for the extra responsibility?

R – Reasonable – Are you being realistic? Set your goals within reach and then build on each small step toward a larger goal. For example, instead of saying you are going "to become Manager", start with "take on extra responsibilities at work" and move from there.

I – Incentive – How will you reward yourself for achieving this goal? Acknowledge the effort you've put into helping yourself. For example, with "a new dress" or "a golf weekend with my friends".

P – Personal – Do you own this goal? Make sure it is about you and your behaviour, and not about the behaviour of the people around you. For example, "making the house more peaceful and relaxing" is not a goal you can own if you live with family or friends. Instead, you could try "standing up for myself and setting an example to the others in the house".

E – Evaluate – How are you going to know that you are doing well? When will the goal be done? Give yourself an early milestone to reach so you can gauge your progress. Measure your ongoing commitment: "I should be doing this three or four times a week". Also think about recording your evaluation, for example "marking on a calendar on the wall every time I did something and every time I forgot or didn't want to".

Case study: Dan set a Specific goal to "be more involved in disciplining the kids for one month". He faced up to the Truth that "this would mean being the bad guy". It was Reasonable for him to aim for this now that his new job meant he was "home in the evenings". The Incentive he chose was "to take the whole family out together to a theme park after the month is done". This goal was Personal to him because it was "about my own reactions to the kids when they misbehave". He would Evaluate it by "keeping a diary and grading myself on my performance – and asking my wife too".

Creating a STRIPE goal

DRAFT GOAL	

Now improve this goal by considering STRIPE...

S	**SPECIFIC**	*What specific behaviours or events can I focus on?*	
T	**TRUTHFUL**	*Am I facing up to the unpleasant aspects of this goal? Am I doing it for the right reasons?*	
R	**REASONABLE**	*Is this a realistic goal for me to aim for? Is it a manageable step?*	
I	**INCENTIVE**	*How will I reward myself for achieving this goal?*	
P	**PERSONAL**	*Do I own this goal? Is it about my own behaviour? Is this goal under my control?*	
E	**EVALUATE**	*How will I know I am achieving my goal? How will I measure this?*	

MY FINAL GOAL	

19.

Worry Tickets

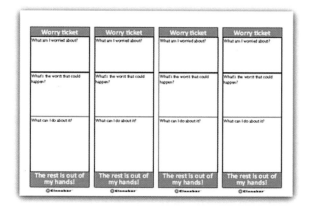

Worries are thoughts which make us anxious. They are usually about things that we have little or no control over.

People worry about all sorts of things. Meetings, exams, events, bills, children, cars, pets....

The list is endless.

Usually our worries intrude briefly on our day, but then we put them to one side and distract ourselves with other things. When the dreaded event or meeting actually happens, we seldom remember how concerned we were beforehand, and we seldom notice that the worst case scenarios we feared so much never happened.

Sometimes though, worries can cause profound anxiety and disrupt our day-to-day lives. They may cause us to be overly preoccupied, unable to focus on anything without those anxious thoughts intruding.

They may even cause us to feel physically sick, triggering nervous complaints such as tension headaches, tummy problems or skin complaints.

This tool works in two ways: first of all, the client can carry their worries around in their wallet or as a bookmark, instead of in their head. This simple trick is a surprisingly effective way to reduce the frequency of intrusive thoughts, particularly with younger clients.

Secondly, every time the client reads the worry ticket, they receive a positive message. Worries usually just consist of negative thoughts and emotions relating to the worst case scenario that we can imagine. The worry ticket provides additional guidance on the positive action the client can take and delivers a positive message about accepting what is out of their control.

Fill in a worry ticket for each worry. Encourage your client to identify practical steps they can take to improve how they feel and write these down on the worry ticket in the section called "What can I do about it?"

Advise your clients to carry their ticket with them and to read the entire ticket whenever the worrying thoughts occur to them.

Case study: Andy was 15 years old and full of nerves. He worried about his mum, his studies and his friends. The combined weight of all of his worries was distracting him during school, and stopping him from sleeping properly. He was in constant fear that he would become tearful where people might see him.

We filled in six worry tickets. He put one into his maths text book because this lesson was a particular concern for him. His worst case scenario was "I fail and have to do retakes and my parents get mad". In the "what can I do" section he wrote: "remember I got a B in the last exam"; "getting it wrong is ok – I just have to show my workings"; "Breathe in and out". Every time he opened his maths book, he read the ticket.

Another ticket went into his wallet for him to read whenever he thought about home. His worst case scenario was related to hearing his parents argue: "Dad leaves us and Mum is sad". His practical steps included "remember they are people too and have bad moods!"; "spend time with D" (younger brother); and "none of this is my fault".

As Andy felt a little better, we were able to talk about why he felt so worried. We discussed the experiences of his best mate whose parents had recently split up, and an angry outburst that Andy's father had recently directed at his younger brother.

⬡ Cinnabar

Worry ticket

What am I worried about?

What's the worst that could happen?

What can I do about it?

The rest is out of my hands!

Cinnabar

Worry ticket

What am I worried about?

What's the worst that could happen?

What can I do about it?

The rest is out of my hands!

Cinnabar

Worry ticket

What am I worried about?

What's the worst that could happen?

What can I do about it?

The rest is out of my hands!

Cinnabar

Worry ticket

What am I worried about?

What's the worst that could happen?

What can I do about it?

The rest is out of my hands!

Cinnabar

20.

Remembering

When someone dies, a hole is created in the lives of those who loved them.

Grief rushes in like a tide to fill that hole with a concentrated mixture of thoughts and memories. These are usually intense but fragmented pieces of the person we miss – a laugh, a moment, a dress, a day at the beach, a scent.

Over time all but the most persistent pieces fade away. Those that remain become our monument to that person.

Use this tool to help clients record these varied memories, thoughts, emotions and impressions – each one on a separate balloon. This can help to protect against further memory losses, providing a concrete reminder of the person that has been lost.

Recording all of these fragments in one place also enables us to recombine the pieces again – seeing the person on the page as a whole. This is especially useful when our mind favours only the good memories or only the bad memories. This tool can be used to encourage the identification of both the good and bad so a real more balanced picture of the person emerges.

Each balloon can also represent a choice. For each fragment of the person they have lost, clients can choose whether to hold onto the string, or to let it go. They may want to release balloons signifying arguments, sadness, or anger. The remaining balloons form a modified image that may be easier for the client to carry with them.

Clients – particularly younger clients – may like to make this a practical exercise. They can buy balloons, write the negative aspects of the person they have lost onto the balloon, and then release them to float away.

This can be a powerful way to let go of arguments and unresolved guilt surrounding the death. For example, "my last memory of her is her crying because of something I said".

Case study: Sam came to counselling because he wasn't coping very well with the death of his friend, George. They had been close friends for over forty years, but in recent months they had fallen out when George had provided some bad financial advice to one of Sam's sons.

Sam felt conflicted and upset, unable to remember his old friend and their long friendship without thinking about their arguments.

We used two **Remembering** tools to record every detail he could remember about George – good and bad qualities and memories that stretched out over four decades. They included: "always first to ask a girl to dance", "had a huge moustache for many years", "hated tomatoes", "bright red nose when he laughed", "broke his leg when we got drunk for my 50th", "broke the door handle when he pushed me", "said I was a bad friend", "made jokes about everything".

Then Sam decided which balloons he wanted to remember, and which ones he wanted to let go. We cut out the ones he wanted to keep and put them on a piece of coloured card which he kept in his bedside drawer.

He told me, "Whenever I think of George, I think of that card. Then I think about what's on it. I'm sad still – but it's a *good* sad. I let all the bad stuff go".

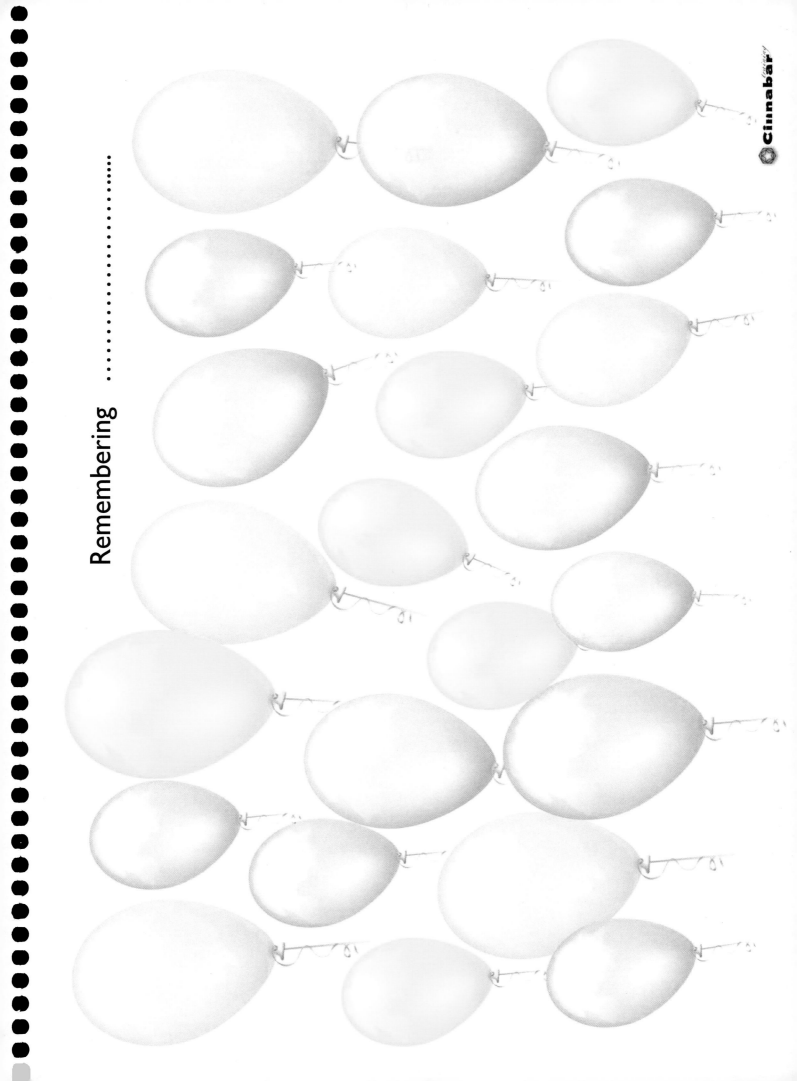

Remembering ....

Introduction

There can often be anxiety that working with emotion means years and years of training and certificates. There is some truth in this, and, as a qualified counsellor myself, I am a great believer that this is to some extent desirable. However, I have also worked alongside some of the most capable, caring, empathic and dedicated people who are not officially 'qualified', but who, nonetheless, are often more than qualified in so many other ways to support children. They bring with them their wealth of knowledge, their experience of relationships with children and families, their own personal and professional experiences, and, above all else, an absolute dedication to supporting children.

I strongly believe that every school should have access to their own counsellor or counselling service. However, being realistic, we have to note that schools are running out of money to pay for such services. This means that more and more teachers and teaching assistants are providing daily emotional support for more and more children. It is what it is, and, although deeply regrettable, we have to do our very best to fill these financial holes with emotional support.

Due to the lack of outside agencies to support children, it is also falling to parents, family members, foster carers, support and social workers to take on an even greater role in helping children explore and manage their emotions.

This book was written to help provide some guidance and ideas for the people who tirelessly support children in schools, communities and at home, in order to help them to find their way again.

If you want to go quickly, go alone. If you want to go far, go together.
African proverb

Considerations

Please bear in mind that not all activities are suited to every child, they may need to be changed or adapted to suit each child's level of understanding and their individual journey. Children need information to be shared with them using appropriate language for their level of understanding.

Some of the exercises ask that the child closes their eyes, to help reduce sensory distractions, and to help the child to focus on what they can hear. There could be many different reasons why a child might not wish to do this, and we need to respect their decision.

It is important to ensure that it is possible for children to take some extra time to process their emotions after completing activities, so that they are not left in a vulnerable or distressed state.

When supporting children, you may need to consider an onward referral to a mental health service. It can be helpful to know your local referral system and how to access other services, particularly when children need to receive in-depth one-to-one support.

1. Grief

How do I talk to a child about death?

This can be one of the most difficult and challenging conversations you may ever have. Keeping these few guidelines in mind may be helpful. Be honest above all else. Explain things as honestly as possible, taking into account the child's level of understanding, while using appropriate language. Avoid using metaphors, which may confuse the child, complicate things or scare them.

- Talk to the child as soon as possible after the death.
- Break information down into smaller pieces, so as not to overload the child.
- Avoid using words like 'asleep', 'lost' or 'gone away'.
- Not knowing can often be worse than knowing – children will often fill in the blanks with all sorts of information they have imagined.

If the child asks you something you don't know the answer to, be honest and say you don't know, but will try to find out. You don't have to know all the answers, and children will appreciate you being honest, rather than trying to change the subject or making something up. Children often know instinctively when we aren't being truthful.

Children might laugh or refuse to believe what you are telling them, which is their brain's defence mechanism as they process this information. Children may also act aloof or ask questions that might seem completely inappropriate or uncaring, such as 'Does that mean we don't have to visit the hospital any more?', or 'Can I have his Lego?'. Again, this is them processing information and does not mean that they do not care.

The impact of grief

Grief is a normal human response to loss, however the journey that each person takes through their grief is hugely individual. Bereavement can affect children and adults in many ways, and it may impact behaviour and mood in lots of different ways. Children are likely to experience a huge range of emotions when they are bereaved, as well as the bereavement affecting their behaviour, mood, sleep patterns and eating habits. There is no way to predict how a child will respond to grief, but there is certain information that can be useful to bear in mind.

When children are bereaved, they not only mourn the loss of the person, but also the changes that the death brings to their world. This can include the loss of their 'normal' life and routines, of attention or comfort, of confidence in themselves or in others, and of the world around them, as well as the loss of security, stability and safety.

For children it can be particularly scary to experience the loss of the living as well as the person who died. This can happen when the people around the child are unable to give them the emotional support they need because they themselves are, understandably, consumed by grief.

Children can become 'clingy' to adults around them, at home or at school, and are likely to need more comfort and time. Some children become withdrawn and quiet, whereas others may become angry and aggressive. Children can worry that they somehow caused the death, that they themselves might die, or that their remaining family members may die – and then who will look after them?

Even if they don't directly share these worries, it might be worth considering talking through them, in case these are concerns that the child has.

Children will often act out their feelings rather than talk about them. Even adults struggle with trying to explain grief in words, so it is little wonder that children do. Children communicate through behaviour, and it is our job as adults to notice what they are telling us by how they are acting.

Due to children's emotional development, it is likely that they will be distracted from their grief for periods of time – they may be unable to focus on their grief in the same way an adult might. They may jump in and out of their sadness and grief and we need to remember that they do not have to focus on their grief at all points in time. This helps to protect them emotionally and mentally, even though it might appear odd to adults: it does not mean the child does not care, it is a normal response and should be treated as such.

When children are bereaved it is usual that they will revisit their grief at each developmental stage throughout their life, processing emotions and experiences from a different perspective. They may wonder what life could have been like if they had not lost someone they dearly loved, grieving for what could have been had the person lived.

We cannot protect and shelter children from grief; unfortunately it is a result of loving someone dearly. However, we can help children as they navigate through their grief and support them along the way. We can try to hold their hearts, as well as their hands, on this difficult journey.

> It has helped to have some ideas about how to get the kids to talk about their Dad and their feelings and grief. I don't feel so lost, or worried that they are avoiding things any more.
> Foster carer supporting children with loss

How grief can present

This is famously outlined as the 'five stages of grief'. People move through these stages, not always in a strict or logical order, and often revisit different stages many times. People spend varied amounts of time working through

each stage, and it is important to remember that everyone has their own experience of grief and there is no right or wrong. The five stages can be helpful to bear in mind when supporting a bereaved child, and may help you to gain an understanding of where they may be emotionally.

Denial – Denial can often be a form of temporary defence, thoughts such as 'This isn't happening' or 'It can't be real'. Feelings often include fear, numbness, shock and confusion.

Anger – During this stage anger can often be misdirected or misplaced. Feelings of envy and rage can make it difficult to support people during this stage. Feelings can include anxiety, irritation, guilt, blame and frustration.

Bargaining – This stage involves the hope that, through bargaining within their mind or maybe with a higher power, reality can be changed in some way. Thoughts such as 'I will give anything to bring them back'. People can often feel compelled to tell their story, and can be left feeling a sense of desperation, intense loss and helplessness.

Depression – This is an important part of grieving and a time when people realise that their loss is real. Feelings often include helplessness, intense sadness, hopelessness and lack of energy.

Acceptance – A sense that life can go on after the death, some level of adjustment to life without the person, and some level of acceptance of their loss.

Kubler-Ross, E. (1975) *Death*. New York: Simon & Schuster

Grief can often manifest itself as a physical pain, particularly in children, and they may experience symptoms such as headaches, muscle aches, fatigue, exhaustion, chest pain or tightness and stomach pains, to name a few.

My legs hurt, my tummy hurts, and my head hurts ... it all just hurts.
6-year-old boy whose Mum suddenly passed away

What do bereaved children need?

After bereavement we can be left feeling helpless, and powerless to make things better for others. We often don't know how to act, or what to do or say. These are normal reactions to have when supporting bereaved people.

There *are* certain things we can do, and put in place, in order to support bereaved children, however. Please note that these are not in any particular order and also that there may be more than you feel are necessary, but this list is intended to give you a range of options to choose from. Bereaved children need to:

• Experience acceptance and empathy.
• Be supported to understand their emotions.
• Grieve at their own pace.
• Be encouraged to express their thoughts and emotions.

- Be listened to.
- Be able to ask questions.
- Be helped to find some ways of managing.
- Understand the reality of what has happened.
- Be supported to adjust to life without the person who has died.
- Experience care, love, hugs, connection, patience, reassurance and understanding.
- Experience continuity – keep to established routines as much as possible.
- Experience good communication between home and school.
- Have opportunities to remember the person who died.
- Have a key person/people both at home and at school.
- Tell their story and feel heard. Sharing their story can help children to heal; they might need to tell this over and over.

How can we do this?

- Listen.
- Be there.
- Accept their emotions.
- Use open questions.
- Refer child to appropriate support when required.
- Don't try to dig too deep, respect what the child shares.
- Be reliable.
- Reassure the child that however they are feeling is normal and there are no right or wrong ways to feel.

2. Listening

If a child's feelings are ignored or denied they may learn not to trust their feelings, not to listen to them, or find they don't understand their meaning.

The following are some tips on how to help children to feel heard and listened to. The suggestions may also be helpful ways of encouraging children to share their thoughts and feelings more openly with you. I'm sure you will already have your own style, skills and ways of helping children to express themselves and share their thoughts and feelings, these are just some further suggestions:

- Spending time with the child, making sure you actually have the time to listen to them with your full attention, can be huge to a child, particularly when they live in a world where parents and families are often distracted, teachers are over-stretched, and their friends and siblings are often preoccupied. Children very quickly learn to spot the signs that someone is not really listening to them and will often give up trying. It can be difficult to find the time, but it can make all the difference in the world to the child.
- Side-by-side talking can be really effective for some children. This is when you are both taking part in an activity together and talking at the same time, often side-by-side. Examples of this are colouring-in, washing dishes, fishing, going for a walk, baking, driving in the car or gardening. For some children, the intensity of sitting opposite an adult, making eye-contact, and being expected to share thoughts and feelings, can feel too much. Side-by-side talking allows children to be engaged in an activity and this in itself may help them to feel more relaxed, at ease, and more able to talk openly without an adult staring intently at them.
- Letting a child know you are listening to them can be done very easily by using simple comments such as 'mm hmm', 'oh', 'yes', 'uh huh' or 'go on'. This can encourage the child to continue to share with you, feel that you are listening with genuine interest, and to feel that you understand what they are telling you. It can help to demonstrate empathy and acceptance of what they are saying. Children often don't need you to solve their problems – they just need to feel heard. When a child feels heard, they will often come to their own conclusion about how to move forward, but you could see if they would like to explore their options together.
- Some children struggle with naming their feelings, they may say things like 'I really wanted to punch him today'. Naming the feeling the child is expressing can help them to begin to make the link and build their emotional literacy. For example, a response may be 'It sounds like you were really ANGRY with him'. Again, this can demonstrate that you understand what the child is saying, and also how they are feeling.
- Try to avoid using the word 'why' when a child is sharing their thoughts and feelings with you. Often children can feel that 'why' is a judgement or an accusation. It can leave the child feeling ashamed or challenged, and stop them from continuing the conversation. Children sometimes don't know 'why' they did something or 'why' they feel the way they do. Using the phrase 'I wonder ...' can be useful in this situation. It is not a direct question, but more an invitation to respond if the child chooses to. Children may choose not to respond, and it

might appear that they have completely ignored you, but often they will look for an answer within their own mind, encouraging self-reflection.

When people listen to me talk about my Mum it makes me feel happy inside, because I can tell them all about her, so I don't forget her.
12-year-old girl

3. My first aid kit

Throughout this book are ideas, activities and tips for helping children to deal with their grief. There will naturally be some that children are more comfortable with than others, and some that they are more drawn towards. My hope is that you can help the child to fill up their own first aid kit, filled with activities or tips that they feel work for them; things that they might like to revisit at another time. The first aid kit can help children in a few ways. It can:

- Help children to remember there are things and people that can help.
- Empower children to help themselves.
- Remind children to access helpful activities when they need them.
- Help children to trust their own inner wisdom.
- Help to build children's self-confidence, self-esteem and resilience.

The first aid kit can be completed on paper: the child might like to create a poster or a pocket-sized first aid kit. It could also be a physical box, using an empty shoe or tissue box. Talk through the options with the child, it is to be *their* first aid kit, so helping them to take part in its creation is key. Suggest that they come up with a label for it that might mean something special to them. Encourage them to make the label and attach it to the box. It becomes theirs — a special box for special things.

There are many ideas that can be used in the approach to the first aid kit. The following are some suggestions for things that the child may wish to include:

- I can relax my mind by ...
  Use the activities in this book to help the child to identify ways to relax their mind.

- I can relax my body by ...
  Use the activities in this book to help the child to identify ways to relax their body.

- Who ... who can I trust? Who is here to help me? At home, at school.
  Helping children to identify people around them who can support them can remind them that there are people they can rely on. The list could include friends, family, teachers, social or support workers, pets, or even soft toys — if the child feels they can be supported by them, they go on the list.

- If it is a first aid 'box', the child might wish to add pens, pencils and paper or some colouring sheets. Focusing on a simple activity such as colouring can help to relax the brain. Any colouring books or sheets can be used, or more intricate designs often known as 'mindful colouring' are available.

- Photographs, letters, memories, drawings or cards can be put in the first aid box or attached to a paper first aid kit.

- I feel good when ...

  Help children to put together a list of activities or things that they find make them feel good or bring them comfort. Lists could include ideas such as: taking a hot-water bottle to bed, smelling my Mum's perfume, asking for a hug, stroking my dog, playing with my friends.

- I can move my body by ...

  Help children create a list of physical activities that they enjoy, this could be a sport or activities such as doing 10 jumping jacks or 5 sit-ups.

- Children might like to include a tub of play dough or a fiddle toy/fidget toy in their first aid kit, something that can help to calm and release tension.

- A worry stone could be included – a smooth stone that can be held by the child and rubbed to help soothe them.

- Children might include a bottle of bubbles to help them with their 'bubble breathing' or they may keep a memory jar in their kit.

There is no end to the possibilities, and each child will create their own individual first aid kit. Get creative, open your mind, and go with it!

I can use my first aid kit whenever I want to. I keep a copy at school and one at home too on my wall. My Dad knows when I am having a bad day too and he helps me choose something from my kit.

9-year-old girl whose Nan passed away

First aid kit drawing

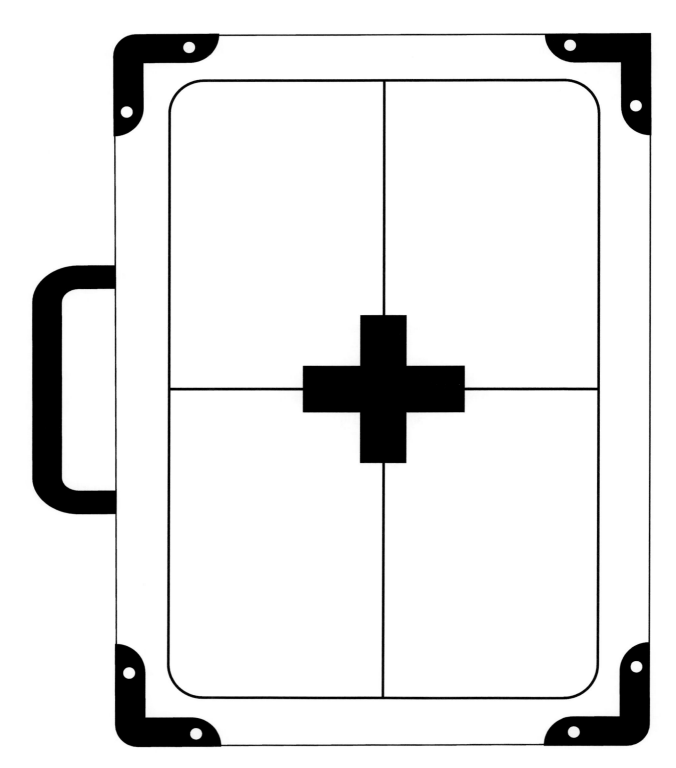

4. Anxiety

It is natural for children to worry when they have experienced bereavement. Children may worry about how the person they loved died, if others around them will die, or if they themselves might become ill and die. Offering children a listening ear, support and reassurance, can help them to talk through these worries.

Sometimes children can experience anxiety as a result of loss. Children who may not have been anxious in the past may begin to feel anxious in situations that would not have fazed them previously. Anxiety is a normal emotion, but when it impacts on a child's ability to function in their everyday life, they may need some further support.

We can help children to understand anxiety, why people feel anxious, how anxiety can be useful – as well as when it is not – and how to overcome anxious thoughts and feelings.

Below is an example of how I usually explain anxiety to children. Please edit this however you like, and if you can fit it to match with the child's own life, then it will resonate even more with them.

Anxiety is designed to help keep us safe from danger. When we are scared or think something might hurt us, our body and brain react to help protect us. If you saw something was going to fall on you, you would probably either try to catch it, stop it, or get out of the way very quickly.

Thousands of years ago there were cavemen and women living on earth. They would go out hunting for food to eat. Imagine that, at the same time, there was a hungry sabre-toothed tiger looking for food too, and it has seen the tasty-looking caveman.

The caveman sees the danger and the 'worry alarm' inside him starts to work. When this happens, a certain part of the brain takes over. I call these parts the 'cave brain' (its real name is the amygdala) and the 'thinking brain' (the pre-frontal cortex).

The cave brain takes charge and sends signals to the body that say, to help the caveman survive, he needs to do one of three things: fight the animal (fight), run away (this is also called flight) or stay very still and hope he hasn't been spotted (freeze).

To do this, there are lots of changes in the body, which mean that we might feel:

- Sweaty or shaky.
- Our mouth becomes dry.
- Our muscles become tense and tight.

- Like we have butterflies in our tummy.
- Sick.
- Our heart beats faster.
- Our head begins to ache.
- We breathe faster and more heavily.

Nowadays there are no sabre-toothed tigers, but our brain can sometimes think that there is danger when there really isn't any. When this happens, the brain can set off a false alarm. This is a bit like when a smoke alarm goes off in the house when there isn't a fire; just a piece of toast that has been overcooked in the toaster.

When the false alarm goes off inside of us, it can make us not want to do certain things or not want to go to a certain place. Even though there is no real danger, our body and brain keep telling us there is.

When this happens, it is important that we get back from our 'cave brain' into our 'thinking brain' again. We can do this by:

- Practising the breathing exercises in this book.
- Practising mindfulness.
- Using the calm-down activities in this book or any others we can think of.
- Asking for help and talking about our feelings.

There are other things we can do in our lives all of the time to help us to feel less anxious and worried:

- Get enough sleep.
- Eat regularly and don't eat or drink too much sugar.
- Spend less time on computers, games and electronics.
- Get outdoors and into the fresh air.
- Exercise.
- Laugh and have fun.

> Now I know why I feel this way it helps me to know that I am really safe, my brain just gets it wrong sometimes.
> A child who struggles with anxiety

5. Helping children to express emotions

Children can often find expressing their feelings difficult, particularly with emotions as overwhelming as grief. We can help children learn that expressing emotion can help to relieve these feelings.

There are many ways that we can support a child if they are unable to express themselves verbally. Below are some suggestions. Please feel free to get as creative as you like: change, add, invent, and use what you think might work for the specific child. Children are often the most creative and skilled in being able to 'think outside the box'. Include them in planning what you do – the more they can be included, the more likely they are to engage in it and as a result, feel able to express themselves in a way that is suited to them. If they feel involved, they will get involved.

While using these activities, encourage the child to connect with their experience and how they are feeling: 'I wonder what that sand feels like on your hands? Does it feel warm? Or maybe cool?', or 'I'm wondering how it feels for you when you pound that clay?'.

Try not to interpret what the child may be expressing as we can often get this wrong. Simply accepting what it is that the child is showing you is enough. Allow the child to stay in the metaphor and with the story that they are telling. It is not always important for us to fully understand what the child is expressing, but that we observe and accept it – to help the child to express their emotions freely.

> It is an amazing feeling to see children start to link their feelings and emotions with their body and senses.
> Teaching assistant allocated to provide emotional support to children

Water and sand

Water can have a soothing quality to it and is really versatile. It can be used alone or with toys and various objects. Glitter, paint or food colouring can be added to it. Often children enjoy simply pouring water from one container to another, and most kitchens have plenty of items that can be used. The water can be used in a washing-up bowl, the sink, the bath tub or a paddling pool – it really doesn't matter – use whatever you have to hand, put down some towels and off they go!

Sand can be equally as soothing as water, and can be used in wet or dry form. Dry sand is great for burying items such as stones, shells, buttons or small toys, for example. As with water, children often enjoy pouring sand from containers or feeling it poured over their hands, which can be relaxing and soothing.

Wet sand allows for children to build more easily: children can make castles, mountains, volcanoes or moats. They may like to use various figures, toys, shells or stones in the sand to tell a story or to play out a scene – they can be as creative as their imagination allows.

Puppets

Puppets are a really important tool in helping children to express themselves. You can use any kind of puppets – hand, finger, sock, string – it really doesn't matter. The child could even make their own puppets, creating their own characters.

For some children, owning and sharing their thoughts and feelings can be difficult and overwhelming, and often children don't have the words. Puppets can break down some of these barriers and allow children to express themselves through the puppet. The child can share how they are feeling as if it is the puppet's thoughts and feelings. Expressing feelings can be scary, but there is a safety in being vulnerable through the puppet, in exploring emotions through a third person if you like. The child is still able to express themselves but, most importantly, feels safe doing so.

When working with puppets it is important that you play along and stay with what the puppet is telling you, as if it really is the puppet's real thoughts and feelings. For example, if the lion puppet tells you he is angry, you respond to the lion about his feelings of anger, not to the child about their anger. This will hopefully allow the child to continue with their expression and exploration, safe in the knowledge that you believe that they are talking about the feelings and thoughts of the puppet, and not their own.

Drawing and colouring

Encourage children to draw or colour their feelings. Expressing themselves through art can help children to share, while also keeping an element of privacy.

Scribbling on paper is a great way to express anger or frustration, as well as crumpling it up or tearing it. Throwing away emotions can feel therapeutic for children, as the physical act of 'getting rid of' the unwanted feeling can bring some relief.

Clay and play dough

Using clay or play dough can be a relaxing, calming way of expressing emotion. The soft, pliable and tactile element of these materials really promotes connection with the senses. You can make your own play dough and add scents and colours to further enhance the experience. Play could be directed, or children could create whatever they like. Children who struggle with perfectionism, or who avoid things for fear or failure, can often feel

safe with these materials. There is no right or wrong way to use them, and any perceived mistakes can be easily changed or corrected. Anger can be expressed brilliantly with clay or play dough, which can be pounded, dropped from a height or punched and pinched.

Music

Movement can help children to express themselves, allowing them to benefit from the health aspect of exercise, as well as encourage the release of endorphins – the human happy hormones. Movement through music can help children to move their bodies and to connect with their body and their feelings. Dancing, listening to music and exercise can all help to alleviate symptoms of anxiety and low mood. You could also incorporate music into drawing, painting, or any of the other activities suggested here.

Painting

The colours and textures as well as the flowing and mixing of paints can be therapeutic for children and help them to express themselves. You could allow the child to express a particular feeling – to express how they are feeling at the time of painting – or to simply express themselves however they like. Children could use brushes or sponges or, perhaps, their feet or hands to create pictures and help them to get in touch with an earlier stage in their development and simply engage in messy play.

6. Memories and special times

Memories

At times it can be difficult for children to talk about the person who has died. Children may worry that they will forget the person who died or worry that it is too upsetting for others if they talk about that person.

The following activities can help to give the child 'permission' to share their memories, thoughts and feelings of the person who died, as well as help to reassure them that they can use their memories to feel close to the person who died.

Memory box – The child could put together a box of memories. They could choose a box that they are drawn to, or maybe decorate a box themselves. Items could include photographs, letters, pictures they have drawn themselves, a CD of songs that remind them of the person, a squirt of (or bottle of) aftershave or perfume, a piece of jewellery, or cufflinks, or anything else that the child would like to add.

Memory lantern – For this activity you will need a clear jar, some tissue paper in the child's chosen colours, pens, battery-operated tea lights or fairy lights, and glue. Ask the child to tear or cut up some small pieces of tissue paper. They could write words or memories on them (or draw pictures or memories of the person who died) and talk about each one, if they feel comfortable with this. Ask the child to glue the pieces, one at a time, to the outside of the jar until it is covered. If the child has lots of pieces to add, they can be layered over one another, just as memories are in our minds – they are still there, even if we can't see them. When it is fully covered, put the fairy lights or tea light inside the jar and turn them on.

Memory tree – Creating a memory tree can be done in many ways. As a school, having a whole school memory tree can be a great way for children to express all kinds of losses and, over the years, it will slowly fill up. This could be a tree of any description, real or plastic, big or small. It could be a bunch of twigs in a jar full of stones, it really does not matter. Children could hang messages or names on the branches. It could be decorated with keepsakes, fairy lights, wind chimes or anything else that you or the children like.

Alternatively, within the home, a child may want to have their own memory tree to decorate – somewhere for them to hang messages or memories when they like, or one to be used by the whole family, where memories can be shared.

Memory garden – Can you help the child to dedicate a section of a garden, yard or outdoor area to the person who died? This could be in the form of a memory flower box, or even a flower pot where a sunflower could be planted in memory of the person, for example. The child can plant seeds and decorate the area with items such as windmills, stones, gems or wind chimes. Create a special place in memory of the person who died, where the child may feel close to them and find some comfort. Remember, though, if it is likely that the child might need to move within the foreseeable future, then they could be distressed by leaving the memory garden behind, in which case one of the portable suggestions would be better.

Memory stone – Making memory stones can be done in many ways: the child could collect the stones themselves or, if this is not possible, offer the child a selection of different stones to choose from. The child can choose stones and pebbles they are drawn to, and then decorate them with pens or paints. They can be decorated with words, pictures, colours or messages. Once the child has finished, they could varnish the stones to preserve them. The child could keep the stones or they might like to give them to other members of their family, take them to the person's grave if this is possible, or maybe leave them in a pretty place or somewhere that reminds them of their special person.

Memory bracelet or Memory key ring – You could help the child to create their own memory bracelet or key ring. Offer the child a selection of different coloured beads, of various shapes and sizes, and maybe even patterned, if possible. The child could choose any beads they like to represent or remind them of their person or, as a guide, you could suggest examples such as a bead to represent their person's favourite colour, one to represent their personality, a bead that represents a happy memory of their loved person, and one to represent their person's favourite season. Encourage the child to suggest their own reasons for adding beads. These are just ideas, and can help the child to begin the exercise. They may come up with many different, wild and wonderful reasons for adding beads in different colours, shapes and sizes. This can help to make the process all the more personal and special for each individual child. Encourage the child to share their reasons, thoughts and feelings that belong with each bead. In a group setting, children may take it in turns to share their bead creations, helping them to tell their individual story, and also to share with others who may have similar experiences. This can often help to create a sense of belonging and of feeling heard and understood. Alternatively, this may be something that children may wish to create privately, and respecting this is important – they may feel able to share at a later time, or choose to keep this to themselves. It is not hugely important that they should share: the process of creating the memory beads is the most important element.

Memory jar – This could be done by the individual child or as a whole family task. The idea is to create a jar full of memories over time. Family members and family friends could also take part. People can add to it at any time, and can also choose a memory from the jar to read themselves or to share with the whole family. It can help families to share memories, and it can also help a lot for them to learn things about their loved one from another person's point of view, things that they might not have known themselves. You simply need a jar, pieces of paper (or card), pens – and memories.

Salt jar – Ask the child to choose a coloured chalk to represent a memory or something about their loved one. Show them how to crush the chalk into a fine dust with a rolling pin and to add in the salt until it reaches a colour that they are happy with. Help them to pour it into the jar carefully and ask them to tell you about their memory as they do this. Repeat with various colours representing different memories until the jar is full. Try to keep the jar still and on a flat surface until it is full right to the top (this will help to stop the salt from moving), then the lid can be added and the jar sealed.

I like to keep my Gran's picture by my bed with my memory lantern. Sometimes it makes me cry when I look at them, but I know it's OK to cry now, I don't have to pretend I'm tough all the time.
A 9-year-old girl

Special times

It is often very important for children that their special person is remembered all year round, but particularly at special times and at various important celebrations throughout the year, such as birthdays, anniversaries, Christmas, Easter, Mother's Day or Father's Day.

Below are some ideas for marking these special occasions:

Release balloons or lanterns – Releasing balloons or lanterns can be a powerful experience for children: it can be a way of sending a message to their loved one, releasing emotion or saying goodbye, to name a few. Children might wish to attach a letter or a picture they have drawn to the balloon or to draw on the balloon itself.

Drawing pictures – Making cards or writing poems or letters can be important for children to mark these occasions. Adults can help by laminating them, if possible, so that children can feel secure leaving them at the person's grave, where their ashes are scattered or any other outdoor places, knowing that they will be protected from the elements. They could also be added to the child's memory box.

Planting – Children could plant seeds in memory of their person, which they can tend to and watch grow. This could be part of a memory garden, or simply in a plant pot.

Christmas decoration – Children could decorate a Christmas bauble or choose a beautiful decoration to hang on the Christmas tree in memory of their special person.

Light a candle – With full adult supervision – a candle could be lit in memory of the person who died. This is not just a religious concept; I have known many children who have found comfort in doing this in memory of their special person.

Most importantly, try talking to the child about the person who died, especially at these times. Even if the child doesn't mention them, the chances are that they are thinking about them. Also keep in mind events such as school assemblies, the first days at a new school or in a new year group, and parents' evenings – these aren't necessarily classed as 'special occasions' to you or me, but to a child these can often be very special, and they can be times when the child might miss the person who died the most.

> I know it's OK for us all to talk about their Mum together. We don't have to worry about upsetting each other, because it's OK to be upset and show it and to all remember their Mum as a family.
> Parent whose partner passed away

7. Breathing

You will need: a soft toy, art materials, pipe cleaners, paper cup, toilet roll and balloons.

We can use breathing practice to help children to learn to self-soothe when they are experiencing overwhelming emotion.

Deep breathing can:

- Help us to calm our body and mind.
- Reduce the stress hormone cortisol.
- Help to slow our breathing rate.
- Decrease our heart rate.

There are many different ways to help children to practise deep breathing, and I have always found that it is certainly not a case of 'one size fits all'. Children are drawn to different techniques and finding what works for them is very important in encouraging them use these skills. Children can add these exercises to their own 'first aid kit' to be used whenever they need to.

We can teach children to identify how they are feeling by teaching them to tune in to their body and breath. You can practise different types of breathing with the child and explore how they feel afterwards. You can talk about what your 'normal' breathing looks like when you aren't thinking about it. Or discuss how slow and steady breathing feels compared to fast, shallow breathing.

As with any new skill, practice makes perfect. The more a child can practise these techniques when they are feeling calm, the more comfortable they will feel using them. The hope is that the child will then use the techniques when they start to feel overwhelmed.

5, 4, 3, 2, 1

Ask the child to name:

5 things I can see
4 things I can feel
3 things I can hear
2 things I can smell
1 thing I can taste

Super pose

This is a great way of helping children to ground or calm themselves, as well as a way to boost self-confidence and help them to feel more empowered. Ask the child to stand how a super hero might stand. Ask the child to show you *and* to describe the position, and then do a checklist inventory:

Legs hip-width apart, check; feet flat on the floor, check; hands on hips, check; or one hand on hip and one extended in the air, proudly, check; back straight, check; chest out, check; chin up, check.

If the child is not naturally standing how you have described they will more than likely adjust their position as you go through the checklist. You could ask the child how they feel before they adopt the position, and then again after they have held it for 30 seconds.

Pinwheels

Children often enjoy having visual and physical aids to help them to learn. They can help the child to begin to notice their breathing and take more of an interest in doing so. Pinwheels can be used to help with this. Ask the child to use their breath to make it spin slowly and quickly or to keep it spinning for the longest time they can.

Belly breathing

Ask the child to sit or lie somewhere comfortable and place their hand on their chest or stomach. Direct them to notice the rise and fall as they take some slow, deep breaths. Ask the child to imagine that they have a balloon inside their belly. Ask them to imagine that when they breathe in the balloon fills with air, ask them to breathe in deeply so that the balloon fills up and makes their belly fill up. Now ask them to slowly let out all of the air in the balloon and to notice how their belly goes back down again. You could also ask children to lie on the ground and place a soft toy on their stomach. The child will be able to watch it rise and fall as they breathe in and out slowly, remind them to make sure that they keep breathing steadily – to keep the soft toy balanced.

Stan breathing

We are going to use Stan the Giraffe to do some calm Stan breathing.

Begin by standing with your feet slightly apart, take a few deep breaths in and out, in and out, that's it. Now we are going to imagine we have a very long neck just like Stan. When we breathe in, we are going to imagine the air going all the way down our long giraffe neck and into our lungs. Try that now, imagining the air travelling all the way down your long neck. Do this twice more, nice and slowly, that's it.

Now, the next time you breathe in I want you to stretch your arms up high in the sky, nice and slowly. Keep them there just for a few breaths, and when you are ready, on your next out breath, slowly bend forwards and bring your arms down towards your toes. Relax there for a few breaths like a giraffe munching on some grass.

When you are ready slowly start to stand back up straight again. If you feel sad or scared or angry, you can use your Stan breathing to help you to relax and feel calmer.

Balloon breathing

CAUTION! If you choose this activity please ensure it is done under full adult supervision, and children are not left alone with balloons at any point – they are a choking hazard.

Ask the child to tell you their worries. For each worry, you or the child can blow a breath into the balloon. If you're confident with how the child is feeling, they can blow the breath themselves, otherwise you can do it for them. Breathe the worries into the balloons using slow and steady breaths. Completing this activity with a child can help to link it to the slow and steady breathing required when they become anxious. You can gently remind them to do their 'balloon breathing'.

Once the balloon is full it can then be:

- Released to zoom around the room – demonstrating the worries shrinking in size as they fall out of the balloon.
- Tied and then popped with a pin to help the child to gain power and control over their worries.

Alternatively, you or the child could write feelings on pieces of paper and put them inside the balloon. Once the balloon has been blown up, it can then be popped: again, giving the child a metaphorical power over the feelings they are experiencing and empowering them to take some control back.

Another option is for you or the child to write feelings on the outside of the balloon with a marker pen. Then repeat the actions above, either releasing it to deflate it or popping it.

I can feel calm again, I just have to breathe.
7-year-old girl

8. Relaxation

You will need: a comfortable place to sit or lie; blankets and cushions are optional.

The following exercises can help children learn how to relax their bodies and minds. Please note, some children may not wish to close their eyes as part of these activities and it is important for us to respect their choice. They can still take part and you may ask if they are comfortable to sit facing away from you, or any other possible distractions, so that they are able to focus. Children may feel too vulnerable to close their eyes but it may be something that they are able to build up to over time.

Under the sea

This exercise is a guided meditation to help children to relax and find a calm place within their own heads. It can also demonstrate the power of imagination, and help children to learn the skills of relaxation as well as of using their inner resources. There is a script below that you can either follow or adapt to make longer or shorter. There are also lots of examples of other guided meditations online or you could write your own, tailored to the child's interests. Please read it in a calm, relaxed voice, ensuring you have plenty of time. Read through it slowly, pausing often to allow the child to visualise the scene and really experience and take it in. Guided meditation can be particularly helpful at bedtime to help a child to switch their mind off and settle to sleep.

> We are going to use our imagination now. Our imagination can be very powerful, and we are going to practise using it to help us to relax and feel good. The more we practise using our imagination in this way, the easier it becomes — a bit like riding a bike. The more we practise it the better we become at it, and the easier it becomes. The same happens with our imagination: the more we use it, the bigger and stronger it becomes and the easier it is to use.
>
> First of all, get into a comfortable position, this might be lying down or sitting comfortably. Now, I am going to ask you to close your eyes and take a deep breath in ... and release. Breathe in ... and release. Keep concentrating on breathing in and out, slowly and deeply.
>
> We are going to go deep under the sea. Because we are using our imagination, we don't have to hold our breath, we can breathe under the sea, like mermaids or mermen, and we are all great swimmers, in our imagination.
>
> Imagine you are sitting on the edge of a rock, with your legs dangling in the clear, blue, warm water below. ... You can smell the salty water and the seaweed on the rocks. ... When you are ready, push yourself off the rock into the warm, salty sea ... did you hear the splash the water made ...?

Imagine yourself swimming down to the seabed below, what can you see ...? Can you see the fish swimming around you ...? Feel them swimming past your arms and legs, they have come to say hello. ... Can you reach out and touch them gently ...? Can you see the bright colours of the fish ...? The blues, the reds, the greens, the yellows and the orange colours ...? Fish of all shapes, sizes and colours, the most unusual fish you can imagine. ...

Oh, there's a rainbow fish ... and over there you can see an octopus. ... What colour is it ...? Can you see the tentacles moving with the current ...? Listen to the underwater sounds ... swoosh ... swoosh ...

Oh, look over there, there's the coral reef ... look at the beautiful colours of the coral: pink, orange, red. ... The fish are swimming all around the coral. Can you see them ...? In and out of the cracks and gaps. Playing hide and seek ...

Look at the sea bed ... you can see lots of beautiful shells ... bend down and pick some up ... feel how smooth one of them is ... and how rough the other one is in your hand ...

It's time to go back to the surface now ... you gently start to swim back up to the surface of the water ... kicking your arms and legs gently as you move slowly back up towards the world above. ... As your head reaches the top of the water you take a big deep breath ... and gently open your eyes again. ... You can remember your time under the sea, and know that you only need to close your eyes and you can return to your secret, underwater world whenever you wish to.

As an extension exercise, children could draw, paint or describe what they visualised in their underwater world. This can help children to recall and enhance what they were able to imagine, and also act as a visual reminder of a time that they felt calm and relaxed.

Still like a tree

This guided relaxation script can help children to find calm within chaos. It can help children to feel more grounded, even when they are feeling wobbly. Practising this regularly with children may mean that they are able to use the imagery whenever they need to feel grounded, even without someone reading the script.

Read the script slowly, in a calm, soothing voice, pausing regularly to allow the child chance to really engage with the descriptions.

Stand up and take a deep breath in, as you breathe in, feel it filling up your lungs and as you let it go, feel your shoulders relax gently. Do this again ... and again.

Keep breathing deeply and calmly and when you take another breath, imagine you are a tall, strong, sturdy tree. Imagine that your spine is the tree trunk running down to your legs and then on down to your feet. Feel your feet on the ground, keeping you safe and connected to the earth. Imagine you have roots coming from the bottom of your feet like a tree. When you next breathe out, imagine the roots burying deep into the ground and spreading out like fingers. You can feel the wind gently blowing your branches high in the sky, but the roots below are keeping you safe and strong. Imagine as you breathe in that you bring calm energy up from the ground up through your roots, into your feet, up your legs and up through the rest of your body and branches.

When you are feeling relaxed and calm, slowly open your eyes. Gently lift one foot just off the ground, put it back down and then lift the other, take a few tiny, slow steps moving from side to side where you are standing.

Practise this tree exercise so that when you feel that you need to calm yourself, you can do this no matter where you are.

Bedtimes can be the most difficult time of day for all of us. Reading a guided meditation to my son when he gets into bed helps him to fall asleep quicker. It helps me relax too.
Parent of a 5-year-old whose sister passed away

9. Mindfulness

Mindfulness is the act of being present and in the moment. It is taking a few minutes to focus on what is happening for you, within you and around you. It can calm your body and mind and bring peace.

The more that mindfulness is practised and incorporated into everyday life, the easier it is to access and the more natural it will become. A child will very often live in the moment, however, sometimes that child can become 'stuck' in their head. This can be more likely if they have experienced something that has caused feelings of anxiety, such as trauma or loss. When this happens, the child can sometimes become disconnected from their body. Mindfulness can help them to reconnect gently.

Mindfulness can help children to accept their feelings, to learn that they don't have to ignore them, or feel scared or ashamed of them, or even change how they feel. Mindfulness can also help children to notice that all feelings come and go.

Mindfulness can promote self-esteem and resilience, as well as reduce anxiety, stress and aggression. Concentration, emotional control and empathy can also be improved. It is beneficial for adults (think self-care), as well as for children. Practising mindfulness yourself is the best way to encourage children to engage too.

There are many different ways to promote and incorporate mindfulness into everyday life, below are some ideas.

Mindful eating

You will need: a few small pieces of the food of your choice – ensure the child is not allergic to the chosen food, and try to choose something that you think the child will want to eat.

Talk to the child about the last thing they had to eat, it might have been their breakfast, or maybe they have had their lunch or a snack. Ask them if they noticed anything about the food they ate, if they could describe the taste to you, the texture, the smell, what it looked like, did it make any sound when they chewed it? The chances are the child may not be able to be very descriptive at all.

Explain that you would like them to do some mindful eating with you.

First ask them to look at the piece of food, what colours can they see, are there many different colours? Does it look smooth or bumpy, shiny or dull? Does it look tasty? Is there anything else you can see when you look at it?

Next ask the child to pick it up; you can also do the same with your piece of food. Ask them what it feels like? Does it feel how they thought it would? Is it rough, smooth, soft, squishy, hard or bumpy? Ask them to touch it, move it around in their hands and run their fingers over it.

Ask the child to put it by their ear. Can you hear anything if you rub or squeeze it or if you tap it with your finger?

Encourage the child to smell it. Can you take a deep sniff in through your nose? Does the smell remind you of anything? Do you like the smell? Is it a strong smell or a gentle smell?

Explain to the child that they aren't going to eat it straight away, but ask them to put it on their lips, what does it feel like? Ask them to take a small bite and move it around inside their mouth. Can they taste any flavours? Can they taste it on their tongue? Ask the child to take another bite and do the same again. Then they may take a bigger bite and continue eating the whole thing, slowly and calmly, noticing the flavours as they do.

Once the child has finished, you could talk about the difference between that experience and the one they told you about before you started. Ask if they enjoyed the food more because they were noticing the sight, smell, sound, taste and texture, or if it was frustrating and they wanted to gobble it down. Try to bring the child's attention to the whole experience, and any feelings and emotions they noticed.

Body scan

You will need: a comfortable place to sit or lie, blankets and cushions are optional.

Lie down or sit comfortably. We are going to do a body scan, by pretending you are in a body scanning machine. Close your eyes if you feel comfortable to, and take in some slow, deep breaths, just like we practised. Breathe in ... and out ... and in ... and out. Now, imagine the machine is just above your toes: how do your toes and feet feel? Are they comfortable in your shoes and socks? Do they feel warm or cool? Don't try to change anything about how they feel, just notice.

The machine is moving up over your legs now, notice how they feel, are they comfortable where you are sitting/lying? Can you feel your clothes against your legs? Can you feel the ground/chair against your legs? Again, we aren't changing anything, we are just noticing how our legs feel, and getting in touch with our body.

The machine is slowly moving up to your tummy, back and chest now. I wonder if you can feel your heart beating? Can you feel your tummy moving up and down as you breathe in and out? I wonder how your back is feeling against the chair/ground. Are there any other feelings you can notice? Don't try to change anything, just notice and observe what is going on.

The machine moves up for the final time up over your neck, face and head. What can you notice now? Are the muscles in your face relaxed or tense? Can you feel your scalp, the top of your head? What about your throat as you breathe and swallow? Just take a few seconds here to notice anything at all.

We are going to stay here for a few more seconds, breathing slowly and gently. Now, when you are ready, I want you to wiggle your fingers and toes and slowly open your eyes.

Bell

You will need: a bell: a singing bowl, or a meditation bell would work well; and apps are also available, which play similar relaxing sounds.

Ask the child to sit quietly and comfortably, explain that you are going to ring a bell and would like them to listen carefully to the ringing sound. Ask them to stay quiet all the way through, and just to put their hand in the air when they can't hear the bell ringing any longer. Tell the child that when they have done this, you would like them to stay silent for just a little bit longer, so they can notice any other sounds that they can hear.

Ring the bell and observe the child's response. Does this appear difficult for the child, are they able to engage? Once the bell has finished ringing, give the child some further time to observe sounds around them.

Ask the child to tell you about any sounds they could hear and what the experience was like for them.

Mindful colouring

You will need: colouring sheets/books, pens, pencils or crayons.

Mindful colouring can help to provide relief from stress and anxiety as it can promote a relaxed, almost meditative, state. It can help people to focus on the present moment as they focus on the task at hand and can bring release from negative thoughts and emotions.

There are many, many books full of intricate pictures and beautiful mandalas that you can purchase or download from the internet. There is also a picture of Stan the Giraffe on the following page that can be photocopied and used to help introduce children to mindful colouring.

I like it when I notice my feelings by doing mindfulness, it helps me to remember that I will feel calm again soon.
8-year-old boy whose Mum passed away

Mindful colouring: Stan the Giraffe

You will need: colouring pencils and Stan outline.

10. Other activities

Colour your feelings

Stan the Giraffe feels lots of different emotions throughout the story and his colours change showing how he is feeling.

Can you colour your feelings?

Emotion words

Happy	Cheerful	Satisfied
Lonely	Alone	Terrific
Calm	Delighted	Relaxed
Confused	Silly	Unloved
Afraid	Thankful	Mean
Responsible	Sad	Gloomy
Worried	Grateful	Blue
Uncomfortable	Bored	Frustrated
Destructive	Glad	Disappointed
Furious	Excited	Hurt
Awful	Loved	Embarrassed
Confident	Proud	Scared
Content	Courageous	Miserable
Angry	Ashamed	Kind
Irritated	Quiet	Jealous
Insecure	Curious	Guilty
Shy	Generous	Worried
Surprised	Ignored	Peaceful
Brave	Impatient	Stubborn
Friendly	Interested	Relieved
Overwhelmed	Loving	Energetic

Using emotion cards can help children to develop their emotional language and understanding. It can also help adults to identify areas where the child may struggle.

There are so many different ways to use emotion cards with children. They can easily be used with an individual child or in bigger groups. Below are some suggestions, but please feel free to invent your own ways of using them too.

You can make your own cards or photocopy the words on the previous page onto coloured card for example, cut them out and even laminate them if you want them to last a long time. This is not an exhaustive list, there are many, many more that can be added, and the children may have suggestions too.

- Choose a card and say what a person might think if they were feeling like this.
- Choose a card and act out a scene where someone might be feeling like this.
- Choose a card and describe it to another person, without saying what the feeling is, and see if they can guess it.
- Choose a card and talk about how their body might feel if they were feeling this emotion.
- Choose a card and talk about what the person might do if they wanted to change the way they were feeling.
- Choose a card and talk about the meaning.

In and out

You will need: colouring materials, face shapes or paper plates

As humans, we often show the world one version of ourselves and keep the real us hidden from view. We also do this with emotions, so this exercise is to help children to express what is inside of them, and what is outside.

Children can use the picture on the next page to draw, colour or write words or symbols: they can use one side of the head to represent what they allow others to see, and the other side, to represent what they hide. You could direct them to focus on emotions, or how they see themselves and how others see them.

It could also be useful to use masks to help to explore this. Children could design and make their own masks, or you could have some pre-prepared, perhaps downloaded from the internet or some oval shapes you have drawn. Paper plates could also be used for this activity.

Using masks can help to demonstrate the actual physical act of hiding our inner selves, thoughts, feelings and emotions with an outer 'mask'. Talking about how clowns paint on a 'mask' that can show they are happy (or sad) can also demonstrate this: How might the clown feel underneath the mask? Do they always feel as happy (or sad) as their face paint suggests?

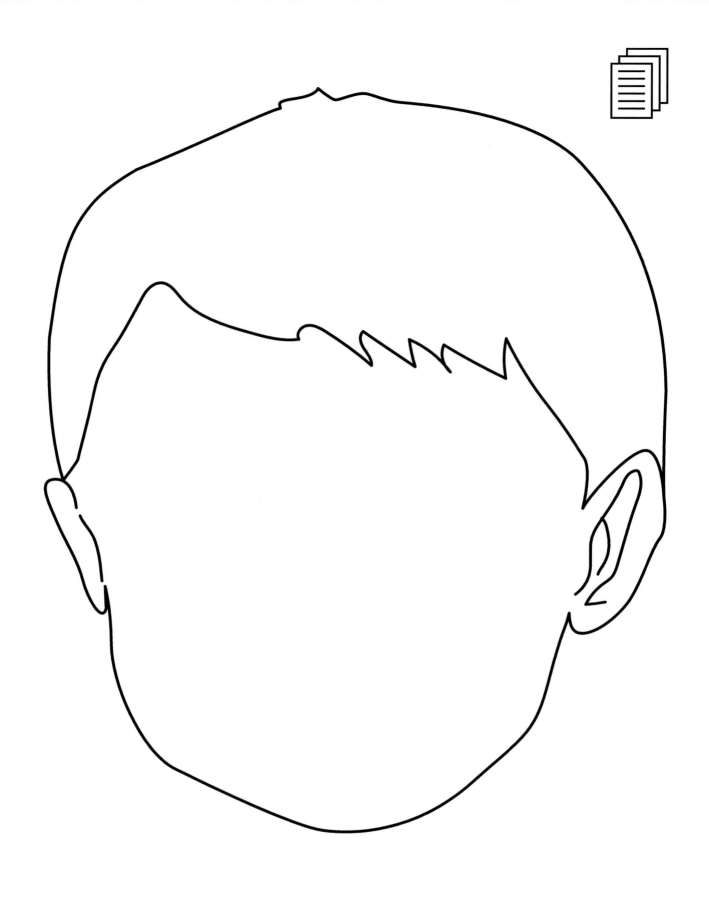

Jigsaw of me

You will need: a large sheet of paper, outline of the body, scissors and colouring materials. Emotion cards are optional.

This activity is to encourage children to reflect on their physical feelings, as well as their emotions, as they experience them within their body. There is an outline on the following page that can be divided into sections and used as a jigsaw. Consider the child's ability before choosing how many sections to divide the body into.

Give the child a pre-cut jigsaw in the shape of a human body. Ask the child to write an emotion or physical feeling on each piece of the jigsaw as they piece it back together. If they find emotions difficult to express, or have a limited vocabulary, you could use emotion cards as a prompt. This can be a great opportunity to help expand the child's emotional vocabulary and understanding by talking through the meanings of each word as it is used. Offering examples of times when people may experience such emotions can be helpful, and might also encourage the child to share their experiences of different emotions too.

Alternatively, you could ask the child to lie on a large sheet of paper if they wish to, while you draw around their outline. They could then divide the shape into separate jigsaw pieces and complete the activity as above.

If they struggle with this activity, you could suggest that the child uses colours or shapes to represent their emotions. Once they begin to express them in this way, they may then be able to share them more verbally, but if not, simply respect this and allow them to continue. It is not always important for us to know what the child is feeling, particularly if the child is not yet aware What is important is that they are able to express themselves safely and without judgement.

You can link in physical feelings to this too by focusing on one emotion at a time. For example, exploring how they physically feel grief within their body, and where they feel it – some children may find that their legs ache, for others, their head might hurt. There are many physical feelings throughout the body that can be shared and explored.

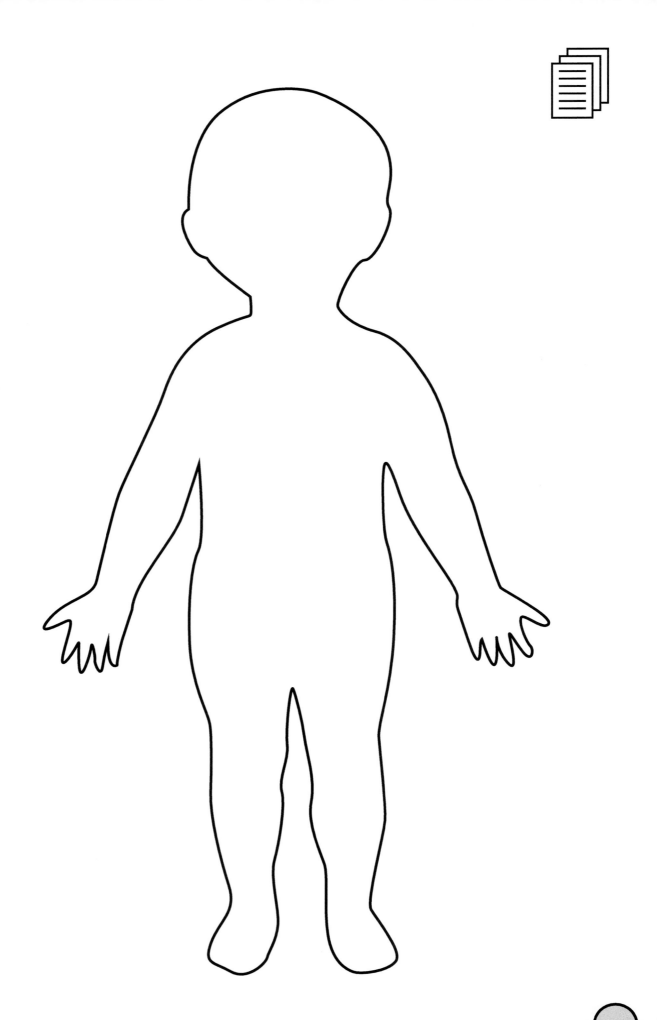

The moon

In the story, Stan the Giraffe finds hope and love again when he sees the moon. He knows he will never forget the sun that is so special to him, but the moon helps Stan to feel peaceful and hopeful again.

Who or what brings you hope and love? Or helps you to feel peaceful?

Draw, write or colour in the moon.

Pillowcase comfort

You will need: card, a plain pillowcase and fabric pens.

Often when a loved one has died, children can experience unsettled sleep. Lying in bed can be a time when they are not distracted and thoughts and feelings can often surface. They may have been used to their loved one putting them to bed or the family routine may have changed due to the death. It may also be one of the only times during the day that the child is on their own, and does not have the comfort of being around others. There are many, many things that can make bedtime and sleep difficult.

Some children might find comfort in having a photograph of their loved one by their bed or under their pillow. Some find that having something that belonged to their loved one can bring them some comfort, perhaps a teddy or an item of clothing.

Some children have found that designing and creating a pillowcase using fabric pens can be beneficial. Children can write messages, words, add colours or draw pictures. The child can be as creative as they like. The pillowcase can also be taken on school trips, holidays or sleepovers; times when there is more change for the child.

A set of fabric pens and a plain pillowcase is all that is needed for this activity. Insert a piece of card inside the pillowcase so that the design doesn't bleed through onto the other side. Children may like to decorate both sides.

The rock

At one point in the story, Stan the Giraffe is really angry. He is so angry that he kicks a rock high into the sky.

What makes you feel like kicking things or makes you feel super-angry?

You could draw what makes you angry or any feelings that you would like to throw away.

Draw them onto the rock on the next page.

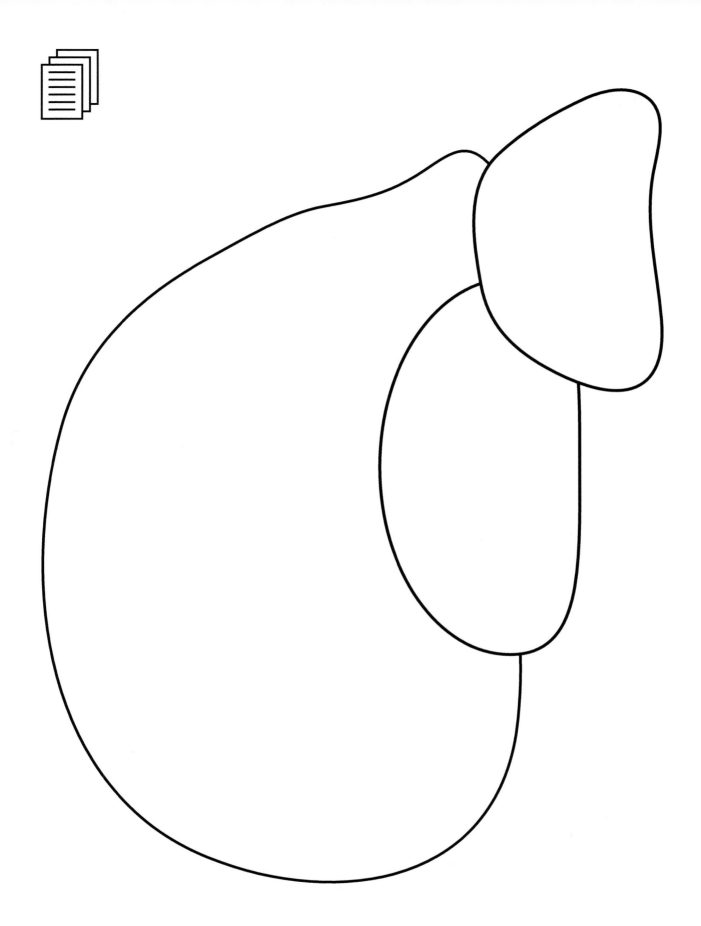

11. Group work

It is important to recognise that any group work that is undertaken is not classed as group therapy. Group therapy should only be undertaken by a qualified therapist. The groups I will talk about are simply for children who will, hopefully, feel a sense of understanding from others who may have a shared experience and who can provide an opportunity for children to learn.

Often, having the opportunity to share thoughts, feelings and emotions in a safe environment, as well as sharing stories, can be cathartic, particularly when meeting with those who have had similar experiences.

When supporting children with bereavement in a group situation, it is important to consider many things. I have addressed below some of those I feel are important and need to be considered prior to any group work being undertaken. These are things that I have found have worked for me and the children I have supported when delivering group work. However, this is your group, so please change things to make it work for your children.

Preparation

There are many practicalities that need to be clear, such as who will facilitate and co-facilitate the group, and how many children will attend. My experience is that at least two facilitators need to be present and roughly six to eight children. It is important to select the right facilitators to run the group and ensure that they work well together, complementing one another. Recognise the strengths and limitations of each person and ensure that their personalities and skills lend themselves well to the task at hand. People need to have a certain level of resilience, as well as being able to demonstrate empathy, acceptance and understanding.

Consider how often the group will run, when it will be held, and for how long. My groups have always been run each week on the same day and at the same time, for an hour, over 8 weeks. Consistency of day and time can be hugely important for children to feel safe and secure. If you are working in a school, you may need to discuss times with staff to ensure children are able to miss certain lessons without a huge impact on their schooling.

Consider where it will be held. My advice would be in a room where there are limited distractions, where the group will not be interrupted and, ideally, the same room each week. I understand it is often very difficult to find appropriate spaces, but somewhere that is big enough for the children to move around when needed, yet without being vast, is great. Somewhere children can feel safe. It would be helpful to have space for children to sit on the floor, but also to have the option of chairs and tables, which could be pushed up against the walls and then used as and when needed.

The make-up of the group needs to be considered carefully. Is this a group to reflect on 'losses'? You may have children who have had a parent move away or a family member imprisoned, or who are struggling with a sibling's move to university, as well as children who are bereaved. Or is this a group made up solely of children who are bereaved?

Before the group begins, it is important that discussions with children and their parents, carers and teachers are held to prepare each child for the group. This will help the children to understand the purpose of the group and what it will entail. It is important for them to know how long the group will run for, roughly how many people will take part, who will run it for them and when and where it will be held. It may be appropriate to discuss what it is you hope the child may get out of coming to the group, as well as there being an opportunity for them to say what they would like to get from taking part and, most importantly, if they actually want to take part.

It is also important that group members do not change: children may choose to leave the group, but it is important for group dynamics that new members are not introduced; this can unsettle children and leave them feeling unsafe.

It is important for facilitators to factor in time to debrief at the end of each session. This allows them time to reflect on how the session went, if they would want to change anything, and to process their learning from the session. It is also an opportunity to reflect on their own feelings and experience, which is imperative to ensure that they are able to facilitate the group effectively.

Running the group

Make sure you are prepared for each session, with a plan of your session, any feedback to be given, and any props or creative materials that you may need. Activity times can vary depending on many factors, such as age of the group members, the number of children in the group, and the children's ability to focus, to name just a few. Tailor the timing of each activity specifically to your individual group. You may also wish to have a few 'back up' ideas to hand, in case you need to shift the mood, either to calm the group down or to re-energise the group. You will need to include an element of flexibility. Although you will have prepared an outline, it is impossible to know what will come up during the session or what may need to be changed. Being open to change, having an ability to think on your feet, and, most importantly, to respond to the needs of the children in the group, is a huge part of being able to facilitate a group successfully.

At the beginning of a group it is essential to set group boundaries and rules. Children are extremely good at understanding why we need rules, and also in suggesting rules for the group. It can be useful to write these on a large sheet of paper that can be kept for the duration of the group and put on the wall each week, so it can be referred back to when it is needed.

It can also be helpful to create a group identity, in which case the children can give themselves a group name, group symbol or create a group poster, if they wish to do so, and if you feel this is appropriate. This can be

a bonding experience for the group, but do try to ensure that the ideas and suggestions of all members are considered.

Creating routine and rituals that are repeated regularly during the group can help the group to unite, and help children to feel safe within it.

Opening and closing rounds: as well as becoming a ritual, these can help children to begin the group, to share and open up, as well as to close and mark the ending once the session is over. The ending or closing round can act as a signal for the group, allowing children to share anything they wish to before the session ends. It is important to try to make the transition to the next part of the day calm and peaceful for the children.

Using statements in the group can help children to share and explore feelings, for example 'I feel sad when …'. However, the statements can often become distorted or turned into something completely different, as each child takes a turn to answer and, once changed, the next child may then follow this new statement. Sometimes these changes of statements can be helpful, as it is something that is important to the child, but at other times, the changes can move away from the intention of the round. Having the statements written down or printed on pieces of card or paper and visible in the middle of the group can be helpful. The statement can then be referred back to by those running the group, or by the children themselves, as a prompt.

The use of talking while holding an object can often be helpful in a group situation. This indicates visually to the children whose turn it is to talk and share, and can be used as a prompt when children are not taking turns or when talking over one another.

Using a puppet as the talking object can also serve another purpose: if something is difficult to share, children can choose for the puppet to talk on their behalf. Puppets can help children to communicate through metaphor and allow them to speak without taking full ownership of what is being shared.

Children are given the option to choose not to share if they do not wish to. Although we would encourage and hope that children would wish to join in, it is their free choice not to do so. Providing that they are not disrupting others or causing issues, children can still benefit from listening to others and being in the group environment. If a child chooses not to share, you can give them another opportunity once the other children have taken their turn. It might be that given a second opportunity, they feel better able to share. This should be outlined in the group expectations at the beginning of the group, so that children know they can choose to opt out and will be offered another chance after the others. It is important that the rest of the group are aware that this is the individual's choice and that they need to respect this decision.

Giving children feedback from the previous session at the beginning of each new session can be very powerful. It can help children to start on a positive note, and can help to reinforce positive characteristics or behaviours that

you would like to encourage within the group. It can also help children to feel reassured that you have held them in mind between sessions. Feedback needs to be specific and realistic.

There is also the opportunity to give group feedback too: this can support the group's development and help members of the group to recognise movement and bonding within the group, as well as help to identify the positives that can be obtained from group work. Statements such as this – 'As a group, you were very honest with each other and you listened really well to each other' – may be appropriate. If there has been a difficult group session, positives can still be found without being dishonest, for example: 'Taking turns was sometimes difficult last week, but the group members were very keen to share their feelings'; or 'You helped each other last week by ...'.

Structure

It can be helpful to follow the same basic structure for each session; this can help to bring a familiarity to the group and a sense of rhythm. Again, this is your group, you can change and adapt these suggestions to meet the needs of your group.

Check in – Find out how children are right now. This could be an energy level (1 being no energy and 10 being bursting with energy), a word, a sentence or a colour to describe their mood, a weather forecast, or a type of animal that represents how they are feeling – it could be anything you like. Choose what works for your group of children. You could also include feedback at this point.

Ice breaker – This could be a variety of different activities, there are some examples on the following pages. They can be used to welcome children to the session each week and to set the scene for the main activity. Often, using statements at this point can be useful, for example: 'I feel scared/lonely/angry/sad/happy/lonely/safe when ...', 'I wish ...', 'One thing that really annoys me is ...', 'I am noisy when ...' or 'If I was a colour/animal/ shape/car I would be ...'.

Main activity – This is the main body of the work and is where the children may take part in something geared more towards the aim of the group, exploring and sharing their stories or emotions. These activities need to be well thought out and planned and children need to feel safe in order to take part. Towards the end of the 8 weeks, the members may feel more comfortable sharing within the group.

Relief activity – This could be fun or calming, depending on the need. What you choose at this point depends entirely on the mood of the group and whether the mood needs to be changed slightly. If the mood is heavy and low, it might be that an activity or game that requires physical movement is required, or if the group members are over-excited then a more calming activity might be chosen. Be prepared to be flexible. My advice would be to have plenty to choose from to enable you to respond to the needs of the group.

Check out – My experience has been positive when using the same method of check in and check out. This can often help to gauge for us, and the children, how each child's mood, as well as the group's mood, may have changed during the session. You could also ask children to reflect on something they have learned or will take

away and use from the session. Some children like to incorporate a 'feelings bin'. A small bin or basket that can be used to throw away any emotions that they want to leave behind. Children don't have to share these with anyone else, and these emotions can be written on paper and then crumpled or torn up or simply put in the 'feelings bin'.

Ice breakers and relief activities

As well as being used for group bonding and breaking the ice, these activities can also be used as light relief. They can be used to change the mood, to teach children skills or to just be enjoyable for children to take part in. Below are some examples and there are also activities in the main body of the book that can be used. (See Chapters 5 to 10.)

People bingo – This can help children to start building relationships and possibly to find some common ground. Children could have a tick list or a bingo sheet and, for example, find a person who: can whistle, likes dogs, or likes dancing. Ask them to move around the room and ask the other group members. If they find someone who ticks off something from their list then they can move to another person, and continue to move around the group until their list is complete. You can set an allotted time for the task and stop the task if the children begin to struggle to complete the list.

Mix up – The group sit in a circle while you name each of them with a variety of different sweet names: for example: lollipop, bubblegum and chocolate buttons. When you say the name of a sweet those children swap places. When you say 'mix up' they all have to move seats.

Guess the mime – Take turns to mime an action: for example, digging, singing, dancing or eating. Whoever guesses correctly then takes a turn.

Pass the ... – Children sit in a circle, you instruct them to pass a slap (hands slapped on floor), click, clap or stamp around the circle, in the order of how they are sitting. If someone misses their turn or does the action when it is not their turn, the whole group starts again. See if they can get good at this, working together to get faster, change direction and so on.

Copy action – Identify one child to start off. They choose an action, for example clapping, and the whole group copy. Identify another child to choose something else, for example stamping, and so it continues. You could add in rhythms and patterns or strike a pose and take turns to choose the pose.

Remote control – You can use an actual remote for this is you like, but an imaginary one is also fine. Tell the children that you have a remote control with different buttons on it that direct how to move. The buttons on the remote control are: Play – walking straight ahead at a normal pace; Stop – signals the end of the game; Pause – stop for a moment; Slow motion – walk forwards very slowly; and Rewind – walk backwards slowly. Once the children become used to these instructions you could then add in some other buttons such as jumping, skipping, and such like.

Guess what – Children take it in turns to act out the use of an everyday object or activity using a pen (or another object of your choice) to help them, for example: brushing your teeth (the pen could be the toothbrush) or using

an umbrella (the pen could be the handle of the umbrella). The children act this out in silence and the other children guess. Once it has been guessed, the next child takes their turn and so on.

Main activities

These are some suggestions for the main body of the group session. There are also many activities suggested in the main part of this book that can be adapted to be used in a group setting. The mindfulness and breathing activities can be used and repeated weekly. This allows the children to practise them within the group, which should encourage them to use them when needed. The relaxation exercises also work well in a group setting (see Chapter 8).

Parachute game: riding the waves

You will need: a parachute and some balls.

The group members sit around the outside of the parachute. Before you begin, talk to the children about grief coming in waves. Some days the waves feel big and strong and there are lots of them washing over you. On days like this you might feel lots of emotions washing over you too. On other days the waves are smaller and more gentle. Some days you might have big waves and little waves all at different times, and this is OK too. Sometimes these waves of grief might come over you all of a sudden when you weren't expecting them. Emotions of grief can come and go, just like the waves on the sea, and just like the ball, we have to learn to ride the waves when they come.

Ask the children to stand up, spread out and hold a piece of the parachute with each hand. Put a ball on the parachute, the aim is for the children to keep the ball on the parachute. Tell the children what the waves are like, and ask the children make the waves using the parachute. You might start off with some small, gentle waves and build up to stormy seas, before calming again to a gentle ripple. Children could take it in turns to give the instruction to the rest of the group, and you could add more balls to make it more difficult to keep them on the parachute.

Group art

You will need: large sheets of paper, paints, paint brushes, pallets, water. Other art materials are optional.

Lay out a large roll or big sheets of paper joined together end to end, and instruct the group to create something together using paints. You could give them a theme: for example, beginnings, endings, their experience during the group, seasons or loss.. Or you could ask the group to decide together what they would like to create. Give the

group a set time limit and tell them that you will let them know when they have ten minutes left, and again when they have five minutes left. Ask that all members take part in the activity and that all are to have a say in what they decide to create.

You may also wish to do this early on in the group process, and then repeat again in the end session. This is a really good way of demonstrating how far the group has come, and how much more able they are now to work together as a team than they might have been able to at the beginning.

You could also provide other art materials: pens, pencils, pastels, feathers and buttons or whatever you like. Just ensure you have enough time to allow them to complete this.

Maze

You will need: pens and maze photocopies.

Children can often relate to metaphors that we use to describe grief. Some children will understand the description of grief being like the sea, sometimes it is calm and other days it is stormy, and sometimes it is a mixture of both.

Describing grief to be like a maze can also be useful. Using the maze on the next page as you talk about grief can help children to grasp the concept. Give each child a photocopied maze picture and pencil, so that they can try to find their way to the end. Explain to them how grief can be like a maze: you can't see the end, there are lots of times when we might feel like we are going in the wrong direction, we can take wrong turns, and come up against walls or other difficulties, and yet at other times we move forwards. Sometimes we need to ask for help to find our way through the maze, and that is OK.

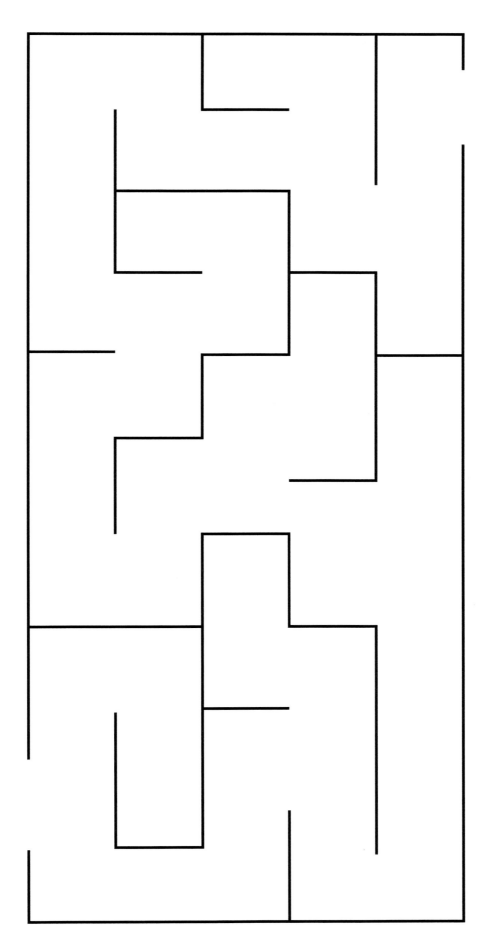

Make a memory sculpture

You will need: modelling clay or play dough.

Give the children the task of creating something that reminds them of the person who died: it might be a memory they have of them, or maybe something they used to do with the person, anything at all they like. Before they begin, ask the children to consider if they would like to share their creation and memory with the group at the end, but that reassure them that it is OK not to, if they prefer. Once the children have finished, invite them to share with the group. They can take their creations home with them.

Mirror mirror

Pair the children up with a partner. Each will take a turn to lead (let the children know you will tell them when to swap over): the leading partner will perform actions and their partner will follow, as if they are the mirror reflection. This can be done with or without direction, but it is a good idea to pre-prepare some suggestions that the children can choose from. These can be actions or emotions and can be used to help build connections and relationships. This activity can be a lot of fun and it also helps the children to practise recognising emotions.

Emotion biscuits

You will need: plain biscuits or cupcakes or paper face shapes, and cake decorating icing or pens.

Ask the children to decorate a biscuit or cupcake (or draw on face shapes) with the different feelings they experience because their special person died. Ask them to choose three emotions and to put them on the biscuit or cupcake. Children could then share a time that they experienced the emotions with the group, but they do not have to do this if they prefer not to.

For example, 'I feel sad when I remember my Dad ... happy when I have a good memory of him ... and I feel lonely that he is not here'.

> In the group I am with other kids who understand a bit, I can talk and they get it.
> 11-year-old girl whose Dad passed away

12. Additional support

Counselling

Many children navigate loss with the support of their family, friends, school staff and others around them. Sometimes children require further support, and this is when counselling may be appropriate.

It is important for school, home and other agencies to communicate concerns to one another, and to consider whether they feel the child is struggling with any of the following over a prolonged period of time:

- Aggression.
- Stomach aches, headaches and other physical symptoms.
- Difficulties sleeping, maybe with getting to sleep, nightmares or night terrors.
- Issues with eating, maybe with eating too much or too little, or a combination of the two.
- Becoming withdrawn socially and isolating themselves.
- Difficulties in school or difficulties concentrating and retaining information.
- Feelings of guilt.
- Marked changes in behaviour.
- Self-destructive or risk-taking behaviours, maybe talk of self-harm or suicide.
- Difficulties talking about their feelings.

Consider onward referrals when they look as though they might be needed and know your next step to take using the referral system so that you can ensure the children receive greater in-depth one-to-one support when necessary. Don't hesitate to seek further support for children: be assured that you know them best, and therefore you are the best people to identify any long-term difficulties that they need more specific support with.

Bereavement counsellors are specifically trained to support children with their grief.

> I just wanted to scream and tell everyone to shut up and go away before I went to talk to a counsellor. But now I know that I don't feel so angry when I talk about my brother.
> 10-year-old boy whose younger brother passed away

Self-care for parents or family members

Remember that supporting anyone through bereavement is difficult; supporting children can often be even harder, particularly if you are bereaved too.

Bereavement can often leave us feeling powerless because we can't fix it or make things better, and, let's face it, when it comes to our kids, we want to take their pain away and make everything better.

The most important thing you can do is to reach out for support. For you to be able to support your child, you need to consider your own needs too. If you need help, ask for it. This is also a great example to set for your children.

Be kind to yourself and how you are feeling, you are grieving too, as well as supporting a child, and this is an extremely hard place to be.

Children need to feel a connection to the person who died, as well as a connection to 'safe' adults and family around them. It is OK for other family members to step in and help provide this care if your own grief feels overwhelming.

Remember you don't have to hide your grief. Seeing their family grieve can let children know that their feelings are valid and OK. They need to see that their adults are still able to cope and look after them, even though they are grieving too.

This book is all about helping children to express their thoughts and emotions. Take note from your children, express your emotions, whether that's with friends, family, a counsellor, or screaming at the top of your lungs on a mountainside, it does not matter – only that you let it out.

What can you take from this book and from the list on p. 9 to put in your own first aid kit? Children learn from us, and the best way we can teach them to look after themselves emotionally, physically and spiritually, is by showing them and involving them, not just by telling them.

> Tell me and I'll forget
> Show me and I may remember
> Involve me and I'll understand.
> – Chinese proverb

Self-care for professionals

When we work with bereaved children and families we bring along our own experiences and feelings of loss. Supporting a child or family who are grieving can result in professionals feeling emotionally impacted too.

It is important to accept that supporting children emotionally is likely to impact upon you emotionally. Accept your own need for emotional and practical support and ensure that you take responsibility by asking for what you need.

If the situation has any similarities to your own life, it may bring back unresolved issues. The very fact that the situation involves children, the most vulnerable humans, can add to the emotional impact on professionals.

There is no way that you can effectively support others emotionally if your own emotional needs are not being met — and that is a fact, ladies and gentlemen!

Ironically, self-care is often forgotten by people who support others in need. We can often act as if our own needs don't exist, as if we can cope with anything, as if we don't need the same level of support as others do. Some of us even think we are indestructible (*guilty!*).

This is not the case. Your needs do matter, they are valid and you will burn out if you don't look after yourself — true story.

Use your network of friends and colleagues for support; they may be the best placed to understand how you are feeling. You could also consider setting up a peer support group with others in similar roles.

The well-known aviation phrase 'fit your own oxygen mask before you help others' is so relevant and true. Taking care of *you* is not selfish, it's not a waste of time, and it's not negotiable.

It is not what you do that matters, just that you do things for you, things that make you happy, that give you peace and, most importantly, that you keep doing them.

Children learn through experience and from what they see. Modelling self-care can be extremely powerful for a child to witness. On the following pages are some suggestions for self-care, like the child's first aid kit, but for adults. Spend some time considering what you might put in your own kit.

A work—life balance can sound like an impossible dream, but if you can incorporate some of the suggestions in this book into your day, you are already on your way to a healthier way of being.

Self-care suggestions

Please note, there is absolutely no judgement here, or expectations for you to suddenly become your own self-help guru. This self-care business that I keep talking about may be alien to you, so look through the list at your leisure, and choose one or two ideas to add into your week. Feel free to add your own suggestions. (May I also point out that by reading this list you are already starting to take care of yourself — winning!)

Smile, laugh, have fun — Doing this releases endorphins, the body's feel-good chemical. Find your tribe. Spend time with family, friends and colleagues who make you feel good, lift you up, make you smile, and support your goals.

An attitude of gratitude — Feeling thankful for all the good things in your life and focusing on the things that we are thankful for can change our mood and, over time, our brains too.

Relax — Have a bath, pamper yourself, read, do some yoga or breathing exercises. They can all help you to relax and unwind.

Physical activity — Whatever gets your heart rate up a little and makes you breathe a little faster will help to release levels of the stress hormone cortisol and increase endorphins.

Get outdoors — Being outside, breathing in some fresh air and connecting with nature can be very beneficial. It can help you to think more clearly, get some vitamin D into your body and feel refreshed and grounded.

Sleep — Consider how much sleep you are getting, take an honest look at your evening routines. Sleep helps us to repair, rest and recuperate.

Eating right (and regularly) and drinking water — These things can all help to keep our mood stable and ensure we have enough energy. Water is needed for hydration of all the cells in the body.

Take up a new hobby — Whatever it is, get out there and do it. Feel good, find your passion and do something you love. Hobbies can help people to have a more positive work—life balance.

Get creative — Art, acting, singing or dancing can all help you to express yourself and how you are feeling.

Social media — Studies have shown the negative impact that social media can have on our mood, mental health and self-esteem. Consider how much time this takes up and how it impacts your mood.

Be kind to yourself — Notice how you talk to yourself, try to add some more positives into that dialogue. Treat yourself like you would treat the child you are supporting, with love and compassion. Please remember, we are all doing the best we can, with the resources we have available at the time in any given situation. I am sure you are doing your absolute best.

Where there is love there is no darkness.
Burundian proverb

Useful organisations

There are many organisations that offer further support and guidance on bereavement, including:

Winston's Wish
www.winstonswish.org
0808 802 0021

Cruse Bereavement Care
www.cruse.org.uk
0808 808 1677

Child Bereavement UK
www.childbereavementuk.org
0800 02 888 40

Grief Encounter
www.griefencounter.org.uk
020 8371 8455

Childhood Bereavement Network
www.childhoodbereavementnetwork.org.uk
020 7843 6309

Contents

I would like to dedicate this book to all of the children I know, and have known, who have experienced the devastating loss of a loved one.

I would like to thank everyone who has helped in the creation of this book; for everything from positive thoughts to sharing opinions, from proofreading and healing to new stationery and patience, from laughs and sarcasm to childcare and time, and for telling me I could when I thought I couldn't, thank you.

To my four parents, I love you all.

First published 2019
by Routledge
2 Park Square, Milton Park, Abingdon, Oxon OX14 4RN

and by Routledge
52 Vanderbilt Avenue, New York, NY 10017

Routledge is an imprint of the Taylor & Francis Group, an informa business

British Library Cataloguing-in-Publication Data
A catalogue record for this book is available from the British Library

Library of Congress Cataloging-in-Publication Data
Names: Rankin, Hollie, author.
Title: Guide to supporting children through bereavement and loss : emotional wellbeing in school
    and at home / Hollie Rankin.
Description: Abingdon, Oxon ; New York, NY : Routledge, 2019. | Includes bibliographical references.
Identifiers: LCCN 2018057110 | ISBN 9781138360419 (pbk) | ISBN 9780429433160 (ebk)
Subjects: LCSH: Bereavement in children. | Loss (Psychology) in children. | Grief in children. |
    Children—Counseling of. | School mental health services. | Students—Mental health services.
Classification: LCC BF723 .G75 R365 2019 | DDC 155.9/37083—dc23
LC record available at https://lccn.loc.gov/2018057110

ISBN: 978-1-138-36041-9 (pbk)
ISBN: 978-0-429-43316-0 (ebk)

Typeset in Antitled
by Apex CoVantage, LLC

Guide to Supporting Children through Bereavement and Loss

Emotional Wellbeing in School and at Home

HOLLIE RANKIN

Routledge
Taylor & Francis Group

LONDON AND NEW YORK

Guide to Supporting Children through Bereavement and Loss

Currently, many children are unable to access emotional support services, and other members of a child's support network are required to provide this emotional guidance and support. This resource book has been written to support children when they have experienced a loss or bereavement. It is intended to be used as a guide by families and friends, school staff, and all other adults supporting children through their grief, to help them to provide this emotional guidance.

Guide to Supporting Children through Bereavement and Loss offers information, education, and guidance about how to understand grief, ways to support the process and emotions of grief, and to help children to express themselves and make sense of their changed world. It covers the 'stages of grief', and holds many practical ideas and activities designed to help children to process and understand their grief, as well as to express and explore their emotions. There is a section on undertaking group work for bereaved children, as well as information on both self-care and what to do when a referral to a specialist service may be required.

This guide was designed to be used by any person supporting a child through loss or bereavement, no matter what their previous understanding of these issues. It is specifically written to be as accessible and as user-friendly as possible to help, rather than hinder, the user. It can be used alone, or alongside the storybook *When the Sun Fell Out of the Sky*.

Hollie Rankin is a counsellor who has worked with and supported children, young people and their families within schools in the North East over the last ten years. Her recent books on trauma and bereavement were prompted by a noticeable gap in resources to help to guide adults when supporting children in emotionally challenging circumstances.

Pass mark

To pass a unit assessment, students need to achieve a mark of 70% or more.

This unit contributes 35% of the total amount required for the Professional Diploma in Accounting qualification.

1

The accounting function

- Introduction.
- The accounting function.
- Relationships with other departments.
- Coordination between accounting and other business functions.
- Regulations affecting the accounting function.
- Understanding systems.

Introduction

Organisations and the need for control

Definition
'Organisations are social arrangements for the controlled performance of collective goals'.

Control mechanisms

Methods of control
Organisational structure
Target setting and budgeting
Direct supervision
Culture
Self-control
Control Systems – e.g. actual v budget
Control processes – e.g. control account reconciliations

Organisational Structure

How to discuss structure
The division of responsibility
The degree of decentralisation
The length of the scalar chain
The size of the span of control
Whether organisations are 'tall' or 'flat'

The accounting function

The role of the accounting function

There are four components to the function

Financial accounting
– preparing annual financial statements in accordance with relevant accounting standards and legislation.

Management accounting
– process of measuring, analysing, interpreting and communicating information to management in a form that is easy to understand.

Components

Treasury management
– includes the managment of working capital, cash, financing, foreign currency and tax.

Internal audit
– examines and evaluates the organisation's risk management processes and systems of control, making recommendations for improvement.

Relationships with other departments

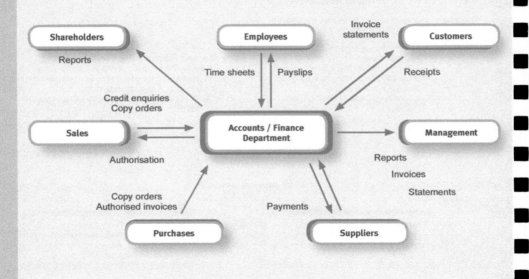

Coordination between accounting and other business functions

Department	Areas of interaction
Purchasing	Establishing credit terms Monitoring payments Inventory and cost control
Production	Cost measurements and overhead allocation Budgeting (e.g. units, quantity) Achieving efficiency and economy
HR	Recruitment and training expenditure Salary payment, estimating PAYE liabilities Reward plans, tax-efficient benefits packages
IT	Systems design and development Improving access to information Incorporating new technology into operations
Customer services	Pricing additional services (e.g. maintenance) Assessing costs of product failures Qualitative feedback on operations
Marketing	Advertising budgets Product pricing Estimating market share

Regulations affecting the accounting function

Responsibility to regulatory authorities:

- Companies House (e.g. submission of financial statement for inspection by interested parties).
- Tax authorities (e.g. HMRC for VAT, PAYE, corporation tax).
- Financial services (e.g. stock exchange for listed companies).
- Regulators, where appropriate (e.g. Charities Commission, Ofcom).

Companies Act 1985 sets out that financial statements have to give a "true and fair view".

IFRS Foundation supervises the development of international standards and guidance. It's a parent entity of:

- International Accounting Standards Board (IASB): aims to develop a single set of quality, understandable and enforceable accounting standards.
- FRS Interpretation Committee (IFRS IC): reviews widespread accounting issues and provides guidance.
- IFRS Advisory Council (IFRS AC): consults the users of financial information and offers advice to the IFRS Foundation.

Understanding systems

General systems

Example – If we are concentrating on the finance system, then sales, production and purchasing become part of the environment, and within the system boundary will be found smaller subsystems such as product costing, financial accounting and treasury.

Control systems

- **Standard** – is what the system is aiming for.
- **Sensor** (or detector) – measures the output of the system.
- **Comparator** – compares the information from the standard and the sensor.
- **Effector** (or activator) – initiates the control action.
- **Feedback** – is the information that is taken from the system output and used to adjust the system.

2

The use of key financial reports

- Financial accounting and financial statements.
- Management accounting and management reports.
- User groups.

Financial accounting and financial statements

Purpose of financial statements

The statement of financial position	Provides information on the financial position of a business (its assets and liabilities at a point in time).
The statement of profit or loss	Provides information on the performance of a business (the profit or loss which results from trading over a period of time).
The statement of other comprehensive income	Shows income and expenses that are not recognised in profit or loss.
The statement of changes in equity	Provides information about how the equity of the company has changed over the period.
The statement of cash flow	Provides information on the financial adaptability of a business (the movement of cash into and out of the business over a period of time).

Stewardship

Stewardship is the accountability of management for the resources entrusted to it by the owners or the Government.

Management accounting and management reports

Needs of management

Planning	Planning involves establishing the objectives of an organisation and formulating relevant strategies that can be used to achieve those objectives.
Decision making	In most situations, decision making involves making a choice between two or more alternatives.
Control	Output from operations is measured and reported ('fed back') to management, and actual results are compared against the plan in control reports.
	Managers take corrective action where appropriate, especially in the case of exceptionally bad or good performance.

Key reports

- Budget reports, detailing budgetary plans for future periods
- Variance reports comparing actual and budget performance, to facilitate effective control
- Reports of key performance indicators to ensure that management focus on what is important to the success of the organisation.
- One-off reports that look at individual decisions.

Evaluating a management report – factors to consider

- The basis of preparation
- The methods used
- The figures used
- The impact on people concerned

User groups

Needs of users

Investors	Need to be able to assess the ability of a business to pay dividends and manage resources.
Management	Need information with which to assess performance, take decisions, plan, and control the business.
Employees and their unions	Need information to help them negotiate pay and benefits.
Customers	Need to be assured that their supply will continue into the future.
Suppliers	Need to be assured that they will continue to get paid and on time and the financial statements will help with this.
Lenders, such as banks	Interested in the ability of the business to pay interest and repay loans.
HM Revenue and Customs	Uses financial statements as the basis for tax assessments.
The public (especially pressure groups)	Will look at the financial reports and statements to aid their understanding of profits an organisation may be making from activities to which the pressure group are opposed.

3

Internal controls

- Internal control.
- Typical control activities (SPAM SOAP).
- Internal audit.
- The purchases cycle.
- The sales cycle.
- Payroll.
- Cash and cheques.
- Segregation of duties revisited.

Internal control

Internal control consists of the following components (ISA 315):

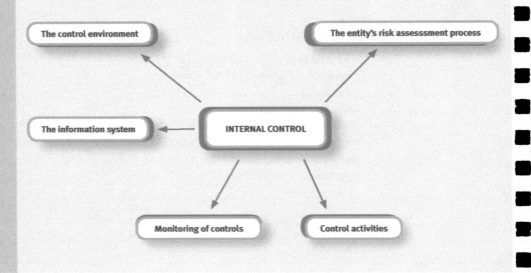

Typical control activities (SPAM SOAP)

Segregation of duties	Keep separate the custodial function, the authorisation function, the recording function and the execution function.
Physical controls	Access to assets and records is only permitted to authorised personnel.
Authorisation and approval	All transactions require authorisation or approval by a responsible person.
Management	Controls exercised by the management outside the day-to-day routine of the system.
Supervision	Supervisory procedures by the management.
Organisation	A well-defined organisational structure showing how responsibility and authority are delegated.
Arithmetical and accounting	E.g. control accounts, cross totals, reconciliations and sequential controls over documents.
Personnel	Well-motivated, competent personnel who possess the necessary integrity for their tasks.

Internal audit

Definition

'an independent, objective assurance and consulting activity designed to add value and improve an organisation's operations.'

What do internal auditors do?

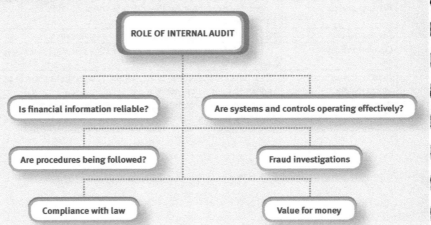

The purchases cycle

Stage 1 — Order placed

Stage 2 — Goods received

Stage 3 — Invoice received

Stage 4 — Transactions recorded in books

Stage 5 — Cash payments

Purchase system

The objectives of controls in the purchase system are to ensure that:

- all purchases are of the appropriate quality and price
- only necessary goods/services are procured
- all purchases and related payables are recorded
- expenditure is recorded in the period to which it relates
- expenditure is recorded accurately and related payables are recorded at an appropriate value.

The sales cycle

Sales system

The objectives of controls in the sales system are to ensure that:

Stage 1	Order received
Stage 2	Goods despatched
Stage 3	Invoice sent
Stage 4	Transactions recorded in books
Stage 5	Cash received

- goods are only supplied to customers who pay promptly and in full
- orders are despatched promptly and in full to the correct customer
- only valid sales are recorded
- all sales and related receivables are recorded
- revenue is recorded in the period to which it relates
- sales are recorded accurately and related receivables are recorded at an appropriate value.

Payroll

Stage 1 — Clock cards submitted and input

Stage 2 — Gross pay, deductions and net pay calculated

Stage 3 — Other amendements input

Stage 4 — Final payroll calculated and payslips produced

Stage 5 — Payments to employees and tax authorities

Stage 6 — Payroll costs and payments recorded

Payroll system

The objectives of controls in the payroll system are to ensure that:

- only genuine employees are paid
- employees are only paid for work done
- employees are paid at the correct rates of pay
- gross pay is calculated and recorded accurately
- net pay is calculated and recorded accurately; and
- correct amounts owed are recorded and paid to the taxation authorities.

Cash and cheques

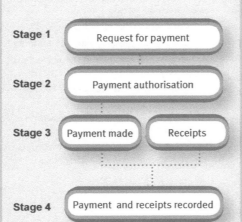

Stage 1 — Request for payment

Stage 2 — Payment authorisation

Stage 3 — Payment made | Receipts

Stage 4 — Payment and receipts recorded

Cash cycle

The objectives of controls in the cash cycle are to ensure that:

- petty cash levels are kept to a minimum, preventing theft
- payments can only be made for legitimate business expenditure
- cash and chequebooks are safeguarded
- receipts are banked on a timely basis
- cash movements are recorded on a timely basis.

Segregation of duties revisited

Purchases	The persons who raise purchase orders should be independent of the ledger keeping function, the stock recording and control subsystem and the cheque.
Sales	The persons responsible for preparation of sales orders should be independent of credit control, custody of stock and recording sales transactions.
	The credit controller should be independent of the sales order clerks.
	The warehouse/despatch department should be independent of sales order preparation, credit control and invoicing.
	Sales invoicing should be independent of sales order preparation, credit control, warehouse and despatch departments.
	The sales ledger clerk should be independent of sales order preparation, credit control, warehouse, despatch and sales invoicing.
	The sales ledger control account should be maintained independent of the sales ledger clerk.
Cash	The persons who sign the cheques should be different from those who handle the authorisation of purchase invoices.
	The persons who are responsible for opening the post, preparing the paying-in details and controlling the sales ledger should be separate functionaries.

4

Internal controls in computerised systems

- Information systems controls.
- Data security.
- Integrity controls.
- Controls.
- Systems integrity in a network environment.
- Contingency controls.

Information systems controls

General controls

General controls relate to the environment within which computer-based systems are developed, maintained and operated and are generally applicable to all the applications running on the system.

Personnel recruitment policies	To ensure honesty and competence.
Segregation of duties	To minimise tampering with programs or data.
Proper **training** programmes	To ensure competence and reduce errors.
Physical security of hardware and software	To prevent accidental or malicious damage or natural disasters.
Authorisation procedures for program amendments and testing	To prevent unwanted changes being made.
Back-up procedures (maintaining copies of files off-site, back-up facilities).	To ensure data and systems can be recovered.
Access controls.	e.g. firewalls and anti-virus checkers.
Hacking prevention measures	To ensure the system is not accessed during data transmission (hacking).
Efficiency measures	Controls to ensure that the computing resources are used efficiently.

Data security

Data security measures involve different aspects:

- **Physical security**, such as the security of data storage facilities, from flood as well as unauthorised access

- **Software security**, such as maintaining a log of all failed access requests, and

- **Operational security**, with regard to such things as work data being taken home by employees, and periodic data protection audits of the computer systems.

Physical Security controls

Fire systems and procedures	e.g. fire alarms, heat and smoke detectors.
Location of hardware	e.g. away from risk of flooding.
Regular building maintenance	e.g. attention to roofs, windows and doors will reduce the risk of water penetration and make forcible entry more difficult.
Physical access controls	e.g. security guards to check identification and authorisation, CCTV, using badge readers or coded locks on access doors from public areas and electronic tagging of hardware.

Individual staff controls

Logical access system	e.g. identification of the user, authentication of user identity and checks on user authority.
Personal identification	e.g. PIN, fingerprint recognition, eye retina 'prints' and voice 'prints'.
Storage of CDs, removable data storage devices in secure locations	e.g. back-up data is stored in a fire-proof environment on-site, and occasionally some form of master back-up is removed from the installation site completely.

Integrity controls

Activities

Data integrity means completeness and accuracy of data. For decisions to be made consistently throughout the organisation, it is necessary for the system to contain controls over the input, processing and output of data to maintain its integrity.

Input activities	File processing activities	Output activities
• data collection and preparation • data authorisation • data conversion (if appropriate) • data transmission • data correction • corrected data re-input	• data validation and edit • data manipulation, sorting/ merging • master file updating	• output control and reconciliation with predetermined data • information distribution

Controls

Input Controls	Validation and processing controls	Output controls
Verification • Verification • Type checks • Non-existence checks • Consistency checks • Duplication checks • Range checks • Input comparisons • Batch and hash totals • One-for-one checks	**Validation** • Comparison of totals • Comparison of data sets • Sequence numbers • Range checks • Format checks **Processing** • Standardisation • Batch control • Double processing	• Batch control totals • Start or report / page number / end of report markers • Distribution lists

Systems integrity in a network environment

Risks

- Hardware/software disruption or malfunction
- Computer viruses
- Unauthorised access to the system

Controls

- Physical access controls
- User identification
- Data and program access authorisation
- Program integrity controls
- Database integrity controls
- Anti-virus software
- Surveillance
- Communication lines safeguards
- Encryption
- Firewalls

Contingency controls

Disasters

In computing terms, a disaster might mean the loss or unavailability of some of the computer systems.

Contingency Plan

- Standby procedures – so that essential operations can be performed while normal services are disrupted.
- Recovery procedures – to return to normal working once the breakdown is fixed.
- Management policies – to ensure that the plan is implemented.

- **Controls**
- Distributed support, where computing is spread over several sites.
- Reciprocal agreement with another company.
- A commercial computer bureau.
- Empty rooms / equipped rooms.
- Relocatable computer centres.

5

Ratio analysis

- Ratio calculations.
- Interpreting ratios.
- Interpreting financial information.
- Limitations of ratio analysis.
- Linking ratios and control problems.

Ratio calculations

Profitability	Liquidity	Gearing	Investor
• ROCE	• Current ratio	• Gearing	• EPS
• Gross profit	• Quick ratio	• Interest cover	• Dividend yield
• Operating profit	• Inventories days		• Dividend cover
• Asset turnover	• Receivables days		• P/E ratio
	• Payables days		

Profitability

$$ROCE = \frac{PBIT}{Capital\ Employed\ (Equity + Debt)} \times 100\%$$

$$Gross\ profit\ margin = \frac{Gross\ profit}{Revenue} \times 100\%$$

$$Operating\ profit\ margin = \frac{PBIT}{Revenue} \times 100\%$$

$$Asset\ turnover = \frac{Revenue}{Capital\ Employed} \times 100\%$$

Short-term liquidity

$$\text{Current ratio} = \frac{\text{Current Assets}}{\text{Current liabilities}} : 1$$

$$\text{Quick ratio} = \frac{\text{Current Assets} - \text{Inventory}}{\text{Current liabilities}}$$

Efficiency ratios (working capital)

$$\text{Inventory days} = \frac{\text{Inventories}}{\text{COS}} \times 365 \text{ days}$$

Trade receivables collection period $= \dfrac{\text{Trade receivables}}{\text{Revenue}} \times 365 \text{ days}$

Trade payables collection period $= \dfrac{\text{Trade payables}}{\text{Purchases (or COS)}} \times 365 \text{ days}$

Long-term solvency

$$\text{Gearing} = \frac{\text{Debt}}{\text{Equity}} \times 100\% \quad \text{or} \quad \frac{\text{Debt}}{\text{Debt} + \text{Equity}}$$

$$\text{Interest cover} = \frac{\text{Profit before interest and tax}}{\text{Interest}}$$

Investor ratios

$$\text{EPS} = \frac{\text{Earnings}}{\text{Shares}}$$

$$\text{Dividend yield} = \frac{\text{Dividend per share}}{\text{MV per share}} \times 100\%$$

$$\text{Dividend cover} = \frac{\text{PAT}}{\text{Dividend}}$$

$$\text{P/E ratio} = \frac{\text{Price per share}}{\text{Earnings per share}}$$

Interpreting ratios

Exam focus

It is important to understand the meaning of the ratios as well as calculating them for the exam.

Interpreting financial information

Introduction

Financial statements on their own are of limited use. In this chapter we will consider how to interpret them and gain additional useful information from them.

Users of financial statements

When interpreting financial statements it is important to ascertain who are the users of accounts and what information they need:

- shareholders and potential investors – primarily concerned with receiving an adequate return on their investment, but it must at least provide security and liquidity
- suppliers and lenders – concerned with the security of their debt or loan
- management – concerned with the trend and level of profits, since this is the main measure of their success.

Commenting on ratios

Ratios are of limited use on their own, thus, the following points should serve as a useful checklist if you need to analyse the data and comment on it:

- What does the ratio literally mean?
- What does a change in the ratio mean?
- What is the norm?
- What are the limitations of the ratio?

Limitations of ratio analysis

- Ratios do not provide answers; they merely highlight significant features or trends in the financial statements. They usually highlight areas that need further investigation.

- Be mindful of seasonal trade as accounting year-ends are often just after the seasonal trend is over when the business is at its best.

- Watch out for window dressing in the financial statements such as collecting receivables just before the year-end in order to show a larger cash balance and lower receivables than is normal.

- Accounting ratios are based on accounting information and are only as accurate as that underlying accounting information.

- If comparisons are to be made they must be with companies with a similar trade, otherwise the pattern of ratios will be different and the comparisons meaningless.

Linking ratios and control problems

From problems to ratios – examples

Control issue	Impact on financial statements	Key ratios affected
Fraud where items are stolen from the warehouse	• Cost of sales will higher than expected	• Fall in gross and net margins
Credit controller ill	• Receivables balance will be higher than expected	• Receivables days higher • Quick and current ratios higher
Theft of cash	• Less cash than expected	• Quick and current ratios lower
Fraud where items are sold to a friend at a very low price	• Sales lower than expected • Gross profit lower than expected	• Fall in gross and net margins • Receivables days lower

From ratios to problems – examples

Ratio	Basic causes	Possible control issues
Gross margin down	• Prices lower and / or costs of sales higher	• Sales managers giving excessive discounts • Theft of inventory • Excessive waste / obsolescence of stock • Cut-off problems • Price rises from suppliers unchecked due to purchase orders not being authorised correctly
Inventory days higher	• Excessive period – end inventory • Cost of sales lower	• Purchased too much inventory due to purchase orders not being checked properly • Purchase invoices mis-recorded • Errors with time sheets

chapter
6

Fraud

- What is fraud?
- Fraud risk management.
- Fraud detection.
- Fraud response.

What is fraud?

Definitions

- Dishonestly obtaining an advantage, avoiding an obligation or causing a loss to another party.
- Note: distinction made between fraud and errors (unintentional mistakes).

Examples of fraud

Crimes against customers	e.g. pyramid schemes; selling counterfeit goods
Employee fraud against employers	e.g. falsifying expense claims
Crimes against investors, consumers and employees	e.g. falsifying financial statements
Crimes against financial institutions	e.g. fraudulent insurance claims
Crimes against government	e.g. social security benefit claims fraud; tax evasion
Crimes by professional criminals	e.g. money laundering
E-crime by people using computers	e.g. spamming; copyright crimes; hacking

Fraud risk management

Prerequisites for fraud

- An ability to rationalise the fraudulent action and hence act with dishonesty.
- A perceived opportunity to commit fraud.
- A motive, incentive or pressure to commit fraud.

Fraud prevention

- Anti-fraud culture
- Risk awareness
- Whistleblowing
- Sound internal control systems

Fraud deterrence

Only when potential fraudsters believe fraud will be detected and when whistle-blowers believe they will be protected will there be an effective deterrence of fraud.

Fraud detection

- Performing regular checks.
- Warning signals/fraud risk indicators.
- Failures in internal control procedures
  - Lack of information provided to auditors
  - Unusual behaviour by individual staff members
  - Accounting difficulties.
- Whistleblowers.

Fraud response

- Response plan:
  - Internal disciplinary action
  - Civil litigation
  - Criminal prosecution
  - Responsibilities clearly set out

7

Improving the accounting system

- Reasons for change.
- Justification of change.
- Implementing changes – dealing with resistance.
- Implementing changes – approaches.

Reasons for change

Reason for change	Example
Regulation changes	VAT rules change
Growth	Old manual approach cannot cope with growth
New information flow	The government could introduce new report requirements
Short-term capacity issues	PC failure
Identified weakness	e.g. need to introduce new levels of authorisation
Changes in the environment	Increased focus on environmental factors
New products	Switch to ABC

Justification of change

Cost-benefit analysis

Tangible costs	Intangible costs
• One-off costs (e.g. development, buying new equipment) • On-going costs (e.g. maintenance, replaceable items)	• Staff dissatisfaction if systems are poorly specified or implemented. • The cost of increased staff mistakes and reduced performance during the learning period after a new system is implemented. • Opportunity costs. • Lock-in costs. Purchasing a particular solution can bind a company to a particular supplier, reducing its ability to take advantage of future developments from other providers.
Tangible benefits	**Intangible benefits**
• Savings in staff salaries, maintenance costs and consumables. • Greater efficiency. • Business benefits gained through improved management information. • Gaining competitive advantage.	• More informed or quicker decision-making. • Improved customer service, resulting in increased customer satisfaction. • Freedom from routine decisions and activities, resulting in more time being available for strategic planning and innovation. • Better understanding of customer needs through improved analysis of data.

Techniques

• Payback   •   NPV   •   SWOT

Implementing changes – dealing with resistance

Resistance

Job Factors	These generally revolve around fear – fear of new technology, fear of change or fear of demotion or levels of pay.
Social Factors	The people affected may dislike the potential new social dynamic (or like the existing social scene and not want that to change).
Personal factors	These, by definition, are more varied as each person may react differently to a particular change.

Response

Source of resistance	Possible response
• The need for security and the familiar.	• Provide information and encouragement, invite involvement.
• Having the opinion that no change is needed.	• Clarify the purpose of the change and how it will be made.
• Trying to protect vested interests.	• Demonstrate the problem or the opportunity that makes changes desirable.
• Dislike the social upheaval.	• Organise social team building events.

Implementing changes – approaches

Testing

Realistic data testing	The new system is tested against normal transactions to ensure it operates as expected.
Contrived testing	The new system is presented with unusual data to see how it reacts e.g. negative sales invoices.
Volume testing	A common problem with systems is that they fail to cope when volumes increase, so this is tested in advance. Systems may crash or slow down excessively.
User acceptance testing	Systems are often designed by IT experts but then used by people with much less IT skill.

Changeover method

Direct	The old system ceases and the new system takes over on the same day.
Parallel	In this system both the old and new systems are run at the same time.
Pilot	The new system is piloted in a particular location. In this way operational bugs can be identified and removed before wider implementation takes place.
Phased	This is similar to a pilot, but it is the phrase used when the system is introduced in stages or in one sub system at a time.

Ethics and sustainability

- Ethics.
- Fundamental principles.
- Examples.
- Sustainability.
- Benefits of acting sustainably.
- Sustainability and the accounting system.

Ethics

What is ethics?

- Morality – the difference between right and wrong – 'doing the right thing'.
- How one should act in a certain situation.

Why should we bother with ethics?

Pros	Cons
• To protect the public interest • To avoid discipline/fines • Improved reputation • Good ethics can attract customers • Good ethics can result in a more effective workforce • Ethics can give cost savings • Ethics can reduce risk	• Increased cost of sourcing materials from ethical sources • Lose profit by not trading with unethical customers/suppliers • Waste of management time?

Fundamental principles

Confidentiality	Information obtained in a business relationship is not to be disclosed to third parties without specific authority being given to do so, unless there is a legal or professional reason to do so.
Objectivity	Business or professional judgement is not compromised because of bias or conflict of interest.
Integrity	This implies fair dealing and truthfulness.
Professional Competence and Due Care	The necessary professional knowledge and skills required to carry out work should be present.
Professional Behaviour	All relevant laws and regulations must be complied with and any actions that would bring the profession into disrepute avoided.

Examples

Accounting issues	Creative accounting.
	Directors' pay.
	Bribes.
	Insider trading.
Production	Should the company produce certain products at all, e.g. tobacco.
	Should the company be concerned about the effects on the environment of its production processes?
	Should the company test its products on animals?
Sales / marketing	Price fixing and anticompetitive behaviour.
	Is it ethical to target advertising at children?
	Should products be advertised by junk mail or spam email?
Personnel	Discrimination.
	The contract of employment must offer a fair balance of power between employee and employer.
	The workplace must be a safe and healthy place to operate in.

Sustainability

What do we mean by 'sustainability'?

- Sustainable development is development that meets the needs of the **present** without compromising the ability of **future** generations to meet their own needs.

  (The UN's Bruntland Report).

- A sustainable business is a business that offers products and services that fulfil society's needs while placing an equal emphasis on **people**, **planet** and **profits**.

  (The Sustainable Business Network)

Examples of unsustainable practices

Economic

- Underpayment of taxes – not contributing to maintaining the country's infrastructure (schools, roads, etc.).
- Bribery and corruption.

Social

- Rich companies exploiting third world labour as cheap manufacturing.

Environmental

- Long term damage to the environment from carbon dioxide and other greenhouse gases.

Benefits of acting sustainably

- Potential cost savings – e.g. due to lower energy usage.
- Avoiding fines – e.g. for pollution.
- Short term gain in sales – e.g. if customers are influenced by sustainability related labels on products.
- Long term gain in sales – e.g. due to enhanced PR and reputation.
- Better risk management – e.g. pre-empting changes in regulations.
- Sustainability is one aspects of a firm's commitment to CSR.

Sustainability and the accounting system

The Accountancy Department

- The paperless office – how much of the paper used in the accounting department is justified?
- Emailing invoices to customers rather than posting paper versions.
- Emailing statements to customers rather than posting paper versions.
- The energy usage for lights, the machines and for heating.
- The use of sustainable materials for the office furniture.
- The level of carbon dioxide produced (if any).

'What gets measured gets done'

- The accountancy function can help champion sustainability by suggesting environmental performance measures and measuring these KPIs.

9

Recap of key aspects of Financial Statements of Limited Companies

- IFRS foundation.
- Legal framework.
- IASB framework.
- IAS 1 Presentation of Financial Statements.
- The fundamental principles of the AAT Code of Professional Ethics.
- The threats.
- Safeguards.
- Uses of ratios.
- Key ratios.
- Limitations of ratio analysis.

IFRS foundation

The structure of the International Financial Reporting Standards Foundation (IFRS Foundation) and its subsidiary bodies is shown below:

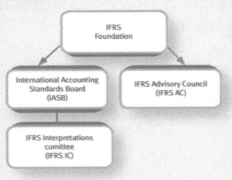

 Key Point

- The IFRS Foundation is an independent not for profit foundation based in the US whose trustees appoint the members of the IASB, IFRS AC and IFRS IC.

- The IASB is responsible for developing and issuing new accounting standards. The IASB issues International Financial Reporting Standards (IFRSs) and has adopted the previous International Accounting Standards (IASs).

- The IFRS AC advises the IASB on priorities in its work and informs the IASB of the implications of proposed standards for users and preparers of financial statements.

- The IFRS IC draws up interpretations if a new problem arises or gives guidance on the application of a standard where unsatisfactory interpretations exist.

Legal framework

- In the UK, companies must prepare their financial statements following the rules laid out in the Companies Act 2006 (CA06).

- The CA06 has been amended to reflect the fact that some companies prepare their financial statements based upon the application of IFRSs.

- In the UK, the Financial Reporting Council (FRC) prepares accounting standards. In recent years there has been a process of harmonisation between UK and International standards and the majority of UK standards are now equivalent to IFRSs.

IASB framework

The IASB's Conceptual Framework for Financial Reporting identifies the principles on which accounting standards are to be developed. It aims to assist in the preparation of financial statements, development of new standards and to reduce alternative accounting treatments.

Key Point

- The underlying assumption of financial statements is that they are prepared on a going concern basis.
- There are two fundamental qualitative characteristics together with four enhancing characteristics:

The two fundamental qualitative characteristics:

- **Relevance** – financial information is regarded as relevant if it capable of influencing the decision of users.

- **Faithful representation** – this means that financial information must be complete, neutral and free from error.

The four enhancing qualititative characteristics:

- **Comparability** – it should be possible to compare an entity over time and with similar information about other entities.

- **Verifiability** – if information can be verified (e.g. through an audit) this provides assurance to the users that it is both credible and reliable.

- **Timeliness** – information should be provided to users within a timescale suitable for their decision making purposes.

- **Understandability** – information should be understandable to those that might want to review and use it. This can be facilitated through appropriate classification, characterisation and presentation of information.

Elements of the financial statements

Asset: a resource controlled by an entity as a result of past events and from which future economic benefits are expected to flow to the entity.

Liability: a present obligation of the entity arising from past events, the settlement of which is expected to result in an outflow from the enterprise of resources embodying economic benefits.

Equity: the residual interest in the assets of the entity after deducting all its liabilities.

Income: income consists of both revenue and gains. Revenue arises from a business's ordinary activities such as the sale of goods. Gains represent increases in economic benefits such as a gain on disposal of a non-current asset and are not normally shown within revenue.

Expenses: expenses are losses as well as expenses that arise in the normal course of business such as cost of sales, wages and depreciation. Losses represent a decrease in economic benefits such as losses on disposal of non-current assets or disasters such as fire or flood and are often shown separately in the financial statements.

Recognition of items in the financial statements

Recognition of (i.e. recording) an item in the financial statements occurs if:

- the item meets the definition of an element
- it is probable that any future economic benefit associated with the item will flow to or from the entity
- it can be measured at a monetary amount with sufficient reliability.

IAS 1 Presentation of Financial Statements

IAS 1 provides formats for the statement of profit or loss, statement of financial position and statement of changes in equity as well as setting out six accounting concepts that should be applied:

- **going concern** – the business will continue in operation for the foreseeable future

- **accruals** – the effects of transactions and other events are recognised as they occur and not as cash or its equivalent is received or paid

- **consistency of presentation** – items in the financial statements are presented and classified in the same way from one period to the next unless there is a change in the operations of the business or a new standard requires a change in presentation

- **materiality and aggregation** – each material class of similar items shall be presented separately in the financial statements

- **offsetting** – assets and liabilities and income and expenses cannot be offset unless a standard requires it

- **comparative information** – should be shown for all amounts reported in the financial statements.

Accounting policies should be selected so that the financial statements comply with all international standards and interpretations.

An entity must make an explicit statement in the notes to the financial statements that they comply with IFRS.

The fundamental principles of the AAT Code of Professional Ethics

Outlined below are the key principles of the AAT Code of Professional Ethics.

Professional competence and due care

A professional accountant has a continuing duty to maintain professional knowledge and skill at the level required to ensure that a client or employer receives competent professional service based on current developments in practice, legislation and techniques.

Objectivity

A professional accountant should not allow bias, conflict of interest or undue influence of others to override professional or business judgements.

Confidentiality

A professional accountant should respect the confidentiality of information acquired as a result of professional and business relationships and should not disclose any such information to third parties without proper and specific authority unless there is a legal or professional right or duty to disclose.

Professional behaviour

A person should not act in any way that is unprofessional or does not comply with relevant laws and regulations.

Integrity

A person should be straightforward and honest in performing professional work and in all business relationships.

The threats

The following are all examples of behaviour that could threaten an accountant's objectivity or independence from their clients:

The self-interest threat – may occur because of a financial or other interest held by the accountant or a family member.

The advocacy threat – may occur when an accountant is asked to promote or represent their client in some way. In this situation the accountant would have to be biased in favour of the client and therefore cannot be objective.

The self-review threat – when work you have previously prepared needs review – you cannot audit your own work.

The familiarity or trust threat – this occurs when the accountant is too sympathetic or trusting of the client because of a close relationship with them.

The intimidation threat – may occur when an accountant may be deterred from acting objectively by threats – actual or perceived.

Safeguards

Safeguards are controls to reduce or eliminate threats. They fall into two broad categories:

(i) Safeguards created by the profession, legislation or regulation. Examples of these include:

- Educational, training and experience requirements for entry into the profession.
- Continuing professional development requirements.
- Corporate governance regulations.
- Professional standards.

- External review by a legally empowered third party of the reports, returns, communications or information produced by a professional accountant.

(ii) Safeguards in the work environment. Examples of these include:

- Policies and procedures to implement and monitor quality control of engagements.

- A disciplinary procedure to promote compliance with policies and procedures.

- Policies and procedures to monitor and, if necessary, manage the reliance on revenue received from a single client.

Uses of ratios

Key Point

- Ratio analysis is a means of interpreting financial statements.
- Users will review the financial statements and make decisions based on the information given. Ratios are calculated and compared with:
  - the performance of the business in previous years
  - the budgeted or planned performance in the current year
  - the performance of similar businesses.
- Ratios can assist in pointing the user of the financial statements to areas where the company may be performing particularly well or badly. They do not in themselves provide an answer but they can help in indicating the right direction for further investigation.

- The types of ratio to use will depend on the user of the information. For example, banks and lenders will be interested in liquidity ratios; management will be interested in profitability ratios.
- Ratios fall into several categories:
  - profitability ratios
  - liquidity and working capital ratios
  - investor ratios.

Key ratios

CBA focus

Ratios are important tools to assist in the interpretation of financial statements. You must learn these ratios and be able to calculate and interpret them as an exam task will require you to do both.

Profitability ratios

- **Return on capital employed (ROCE) =**

$$\frac{\text{Profit from operations}}{\text{Total equity} + \text{Non-current liabilities}} \times 100$$

  ROCE is very important as it shows the profit generated from the capital employed in the business. If ROCE has increased it is due to either increases in profitability and/or increases in asset utilisation.

- **Return on shareholder's funds =**

$$\frac{\text{Profit after tax}}{\text{Total equity}} \times 100$$

- **Gross profit percentage =**

$$\frac{\text{Gross profit}}{\text{Revenue}} \times 100$$

  This shows the profit made on revenue before accounting for overhead costs. An increase or decrease may be due to a change in the sales mix, changes in costs or selling prices.

- **Expense/Revenue percentage**

$$\frac{\text{Specified expense}}{\text{Revenue}} \times 100$$

- This can apply to any expense

- **Operating profit percentage =**

$$\frac{\text{Profit from operations}}{\text{Revenue}} \times 100$$

This shows the profitability after taking into account expenses. A change may be due to changes in costs. You might expect an increase if sales have increased, but must watch out for costs that are rising above any sales increase as it may be that costs are not being controlled.

Liquidity

- **The current ratio =**

$$\frac{\text{Current assets}}{\text{Current liabilities}}$$

- **The quick ratio =**

$$\frac{\text{Current assets} - \text{inventory}}{\text{Current liabilities}}$$

These two ratios show whether a business can cover its current liabilities from current assets. The quick ratio removes inventory as this is the least liquid current asset. If the ratio is too low, it may suggest the business will have trouble paying current liabilities and if the ratio is too high it may suggest that working capital is not being used efficiently.

This ratio can vary greatly from industry to industry.

Use of resources

- **Inventory turnover =**

$$\frac{\text{Cost of sales}}{\text{Inventories}}$$

- Companies have to strike a balance between being able to satisfy customers' requirements from inventory and the cost of having too much capital tied up in inventory.

- **Inventory holding period =**

$$\frac{\text{Inventories}}{\text{Cost of sales}} \times 365 \text{ days}$$

This shows how long inventory is being held before use.

- **Asset turnover (net assets) =**

$$\frac{\text{Revenue}}{\text{Total assets - current liabilities}}$$

- **Trade receivables collection period =**

$$\frac{\text{Trade receivables}}{\text{Revenue}} \times 365 \text{ days}$$

If the receivables collection period becomes too high, the business may suffer from poor cash flow. Retail companies do not usually have receivables so this ratio would be irrelevant for those companies.

- **Trade payables payment period =**

$$\frac{\text{Trade payables}}{\text{Cost of sales}} \times 365 \text{ days}$$

Extending the payables payment period can be a cheap source of finance but companies run the risk of upsetting suppliers and not being offered credit in the future.

- **Working Capital Cycle =**
Inventory days + Receivables days – Payables days.

- **Asset turnover (non-current assets) =**

$$\frac{\text{Revenue}}{\text{non-current assets}}$$

Financial position

- **Interest cover =**

$$\frac{\text{Profit from operations}}{\text{Finance costs}}$$

- This shows how many times the interest charge can be paid out of the current profits. It is a measure of security - the higher the ratio, the more secure the interest payment.

- **Gearing =**

$$\frac{\text{Non-current liabilities}}{\text{Total equity + Non-current liabilities}}$$

- This ratio shows the proportion of debt to total finance in the business (equity plus debt). The higher the gearing ratio, the riskier a company is seen to be as debt interest must be paid out before dividends.

Limitations of ratio analysis

- Ratios do not provide answers; they merely highlight significant features or trends in the financial statements. They usually highlight areas that need further investigation.

- Be mindful of seasonal trade as accounting year-ends are often just after the seasonal trend is over when the business is at its best.

- Watch out for window dressing in the financial statements such as collecting receivables just before the year-end in order to show a larger cash balance and lower receivables than is normal.

- Accounting ratios are based on accounting information and are only as accurate as that underlying accounting information.

- If comparisons are to be made they must be with companies with a similar trade, otherwise the pattern of ratios will be different and the comparisons meaningless.

10

Recap of key aspects of Management Accounting: Budgeting

- Behavioural aspects of budgeting.
- Basic methods of budgeting.
- Flexed budgets.
- Flexible budgets.
- Materials variances.
- Labour variances.
- Interdependence of variances.
- Variance investigation.
- Reasons for variances.
- Performance indicators.

Behavioural aspects of budgeting

Target setting and motivation

Targets will assist motivation and appraisal if they are at the right level.

- Too hard and people give up.
- Too easy and people won't try hard enough.

An ideal target should be slightly above the anticipated performance level.

Targets should be:

- Communicated in advance.
- Dependent on factors controllable by the individual.
- Based on quantifiable factors.
- Linked to appropriate rewards and penalties.
- Chosen carefully to ensure goal congruence.
- Challenging but achievable.

Participation is generally agreed to help.

Participation

Top-down budgeting (non-participative)

A budget which is set without allowing the ultimate budget holder to have the opportunity to participate in the budgeting process.

Bottom-up budgeting (participative)

A system of budgeting in which budget holders have the opportunity to participate in setting their own budgets.

Advantages of participative budgets	Disadvantages of participative budgets
1. Increased motivation.	1. Senior managers may resent loss of control.
2. Should contain better information, especially in a fast-moving or diverse business.	2. Bad decisions from inexperienced managers.
3. Increases managers' understanding and commitment.	3. Budgets may not be in line with corporate objectives.
4. Better communication.	4. Budget preparation is slower and disputes can arise.
5. Senior managers can concentrate on strategy.	5. Figures may be subject to bias if junior managers either try to impress or set easily achievable targets (budgetary slack).
	6. Certain environments may preclude participation, e.g. sales manager may be faced with long-term contracts already agreed.

Basic methods of budgeting

Incremental (historic)	Zero-based budgeting	Priority-based budgeting	Activity-based budgeting
Starts with previous period's budget or actual results and adds (or subtracts) an incremental amount to cover inflation and other known changes.	Requires cost element to be specifically justified, as though the activities to which the budget relates were being undertaken for the first time.	A competitively ranked listing of high to low priority discrete bids for "decision packages." • All activities are re-evaluated each time a budget is set. • Does not require a zero assumption.	Preparing budgets using overhead costs from activity based costing methodology.
Suitable for stable businesses, where costs are not expected to change significantly.	Without approval, the budget allowance is zero.		
There should be good cost control and limited discretionary costs.	Suitable for allocating resources in areas were spend is discretionary.		

Flexed budgets

For variances to be meaningful and appropriate for use as decision-making tools, a **flexed budget** should be prepared to take into account the change between the budgeted levels of activity (sales and production) and the actual levels.

	Budget	**Flexed budget**	**Actual**
Sales volume	100 units	90 units	90 units
Sales value	£1,000	£900	£990
Variable costs	£500	£450	£495
Fixed costs	£200	£200	£210
Profit	£300	£250	£285

Flexible budgets

A **fixed** budget contains information on costs and revenue for one level of activity. A **flexible** budget shows the same information, but for a number of different levels of activity.

	Low	Normal	High
Activity level	80,000 units	100,000 units	120,000 units
Revenue	£3,200,000	£4,000,000	£4,800,000
Variable costs	£1,440,000	£1,800,000	£2,160,000
Fixed costs	£300,000	£300,000	£300,000
Profit	£1,460,000	£1,900,000	£2,340,000

A **flexible** budget model makes it possible to quickly amend the line items in the event of some unforeseen complication. For example, should sales volume suddenly drop, affecting the amount of generated revenue, the flexible format makes it easy to quickly change the amounts associated with specific line items to reflect the new set of circumstances.

The ability to quickly adjust a flexible budget to take into account changes in output levels or shifts in income means that a business can move quickly to meet the new circumstances. By contrast, a fixed budget, that is based on a single set of projections and allows no room for adjustments without going through a complicated approval process, wastes valuable time and money that could be used more efficiently.

Materials variances

1 Materials price variance

The material price variance is calculated compared to what we expected to pay, so that we can work out whether we have paid too much or too little for our materials.

We always use the **Purchased quantity** in the calculation and we compare the Actual price paid and the **Standard** (expected) price.

Formula:	
Actual quantity purchased × Actual price V Actual quantity purchased × Standard price	
Materials price variance	£X F/ A

We can also use what we call the Did and Should method to work out an answer.

x units did cost	£X
x units should have cost @ £x	£X
Variance	£X F/A

2 Materials Usage variance

The materials usage variance is calculated so that we can work out whether we have used too much or too little material to manufacture our goods in the period.

We always use the Used quantity of material in the calculation, and we compare the Actual amount of materials used with the Standard (expected) amount of materials that we should use to make the actual volume of goods in the period (the activity level).

Formula:	
Actual quantity used × Standard price V Standard quantity used for actual production × Standard price	
Materials usage variance	£X F/A

We can also use what we call the Did and Should method to work out an answer.

x units did use	x	kgs
x units should have used @ 2 sq metres per box	x	kgs
	x	kgs
Multiplied by the standard (expected) price	*£x	
So variance is	£X	

Labour variances

1 Labour rate variance

The labour rate variance is calculated so that we can work out whether or not we have paid the correct hourly rate to the direct labour employees. We always use the total hours paid and we compare the Actual hourly rate paid and the standard (expected) hourly rate.

Formula:	
Actual labour hours paid × Actual rate V Actual labour hours paid × Standard rate	
Labour rate variance	£X F/A

When calculating the labour rate variance we could again use what we call the Did and Should method to work out the answer.

x hours did cost	£X
x hours should have cost @ £X per hour	£X
Variance	£X

2 Labour efficiency variance

The labour efficiency variance is calculated so that we can work out whether we have used too much or too little labour to manufacture our goods in the period.

We always use the worked quantity of hours and we compare the actual number of hours worked and the standard (expected) number of hours that we should work to make the volume of goods in the period (the activity level).

Formula:

Actual hours worked × Standard rate
V
Standard hours worked for actual production × Standard rate

Labour efficiency variance   £X F/A

We can use the Did and Should method to calculate the labour efficiency also.

X units did use	X hours
X units should have used @ x minutes per box	X hours
	X hours
Multiplied by the standard (expected) rate	× £X per hour
so variance is	£X

3 Idle time variance

The idle time variance is calculated as the difference between the direct labour hours paid and the direct labour hours worked. It is a balancing figure and it is always adverse. It is always calculated using the standard (expected) hourly rate.

Actual hours paid × Standard rate
V
Actual hours worked × Standard rate

Hours paid for	X hours
Hours worked	X hours
	X hours
Multiplied by the standard (expected) rate	× £X per hour
so variance is	£X F / A

Interdependence of variances

The cause of a variance may affect another variance in a corresponding or opposite way.

For example, workers trying to improve productivity (favourable labour efficiency variance) might become careless and waste more material (adverse material usage variance).

Variance investigation

Variance calculations are just the starting point. Next, management need to decide which variances are worth investigating. To do this they will consider the following.

- How big is the variance?
  - Absolute size
  - Relative size as a % of standard
  - Overall trend.
- Is it favourable or adverse?
- Possible reasons for it
  - Planning errors
  - Measurement problems
  - Random factors
  - Operational issues.
- Controllability.
- Cost v benefit of investigation.

- Likelihood of a problem, based on past experience.
- The overall picture given by all the variances.

Management will seek to assign responsibility for the variances so they can be investigated further.

Reasons for variances

Variance		Possible causes	Variance		Possible causes
Materials:	Price	Bulk discounts		Efficiency	Different levels of skill
		Different suppliers/ Different materials			Different working conditions
		Unexpected delivery costs			The learning effect
		Different buying procedures			Lack of supervision
	Usage	Different quality material			Works to rule
		Theft, obsolescence, deterioration			Machine breakdowns
		Different quality of staff			Lack of material
		Different mix of material			Lack of orders
		Different batch sizes and trim loss			Strikes (if paid)
Labour:	Rate	Different class of labour			Too long over coffee breaks
		Excessive overtime	Overhead:	Price	Change in nature of overhead
		Productivity bonuses			Unforeseen price changes
		National wage negotiations		Volume	Excessive idle time
		Union action			Increase in workforce

Performance indicators

The examiner has grouped these measures into four areas:

1   **Quality** indicators such as reject rates.

2   **Efficiency indicators,** such as the number of products made per labour hour, or idle time ratios.

3   **Capacity measures,** such as machine utilisation ratios (or 'asset utilisation' ratios).

4   **Simple financial measures** such as the average selling price, profit percentage of sales revenue, material cost of material per unit of purchase, labour rate per hour, cost per unit of production and sales and cost variances.

11

Recap of key aspects of Management Accounting: Decision and control

- Differences between absorption and marginal costing.
- MC and TAC – Summary.
- Breakeven analysis.
- Limiting factors.
- Standard costing.
- Variance analysis – overview.
- Materials variances.
- Labour variances.
- Variable overhead variances.
- Fixed overhead variances.

- Variance investigation.
- Performance measurement.
- Profitability ratios.
- Liquidity ratios.
- Working capital ratios.
- Investor ratio.
- The balanced scorecard.
- Lifecycle costing.
- Target costing.
- Activity Based Costing (ABC).

Differences between absorption and marginal costing

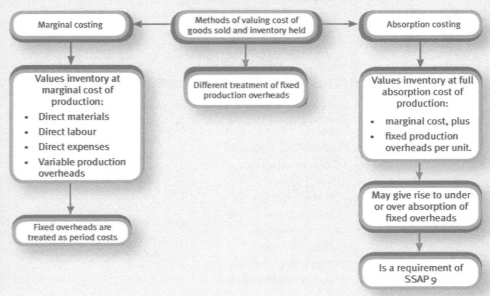

Marginal costing ← Methods of valuing cost of goods sold and inventory held → Absorption costing

Different treatment of fixed production overheads

Values inventory at marginal cost of production:
- Direct materials
- Direct labour
- Direct expenses
- Variable production overheads

Fixed overheads are treated as period costs

Values inventory at full absorption cost of production:
- marginal cost, plus
- fixed production overheads per unit.

May give rise to under or over absorption of fixed overheads

Is a requirement of SSAP 9

MC and TAC – summary

Marginal costing (MC)

In marginal costing, units of inventory are valued incorporating only variable production costs.

- More consistent with short term decision making techniques as most focus on contribution.
- Can also be simpler as fixed costs do not have to be apportioned.
- Cannot boost profit simply by making more units (unlike TAC).

Total absorption costing

In absorption costing, inventories are valued by incorporating all production costs, both fixed and variable.

- Suitable for financial reporting.
- Suitable for 'full cost plus' pricing, ensuring that all costs are covered.

- Profit fluctuates less when faced with seasonal trade.

Overhead absorption is achieved by means of a predetermined Overhead Absorption Rate (OAR).

Breakeven analysis

Breakeven point

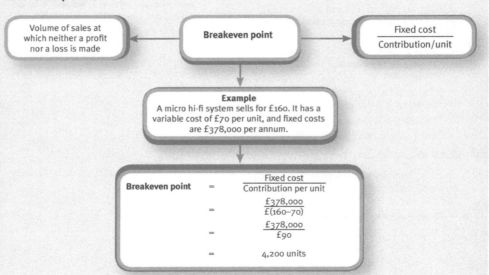

Volume of sales at which neither a profit nor a loss is made	← **Breakeven point** →	$\dfrac{\text{Fixed cost}}{\text{Contribution/unit}}$

Example

A micro hi-fi system sells for £160. It has a variable cost of £70 per unit, and fixed costs are £378,000 per annum.

$$
\begin{aligned}
\textbf{Breakeven point} \quad &= \quad \frac{\text{Fixed cost}}{\text{Contribution per unit}} \\[6pt]
&= \quad \frac{£378{,}000}{£(160-70)} \\[6pt]
&= \quad \frac{£378{,}000}{£90} \\[6pt]
&= \quad 4{,}200 \text{ units}
\end{aligned}
$$

Margin of safety

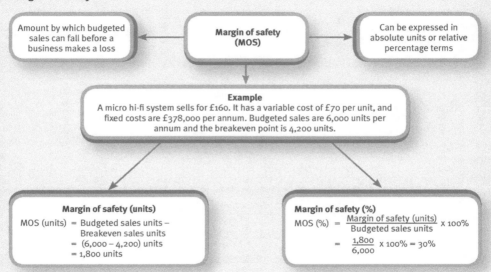

Amount by which budgeted sales can fall before a business makes a loss

Margin of safety (MOS)

Can be expressed in absolute units or relative percentage terms

Example
A micro hi-fi system sells for £160. It has a variable cost of £70 per unit, and fixed costs are £378,000 per annum. Budgeted sales are 6,000 units per annum and the breakeven point is 4,200 units.

Margin of safety (units)
MOS (units) = Budgeted sales units – Breakeven sales units
= (6,000 – 4,200) units
= 1,800 units

Margin of safety (%)
MOS (%) = $\dfrac{\text{Margin of safety (units)}}{\text{Budgeted sales units}} \times 100\%$
= $\dfrac{1,800}{6,000} \times 100\% = 30\%$

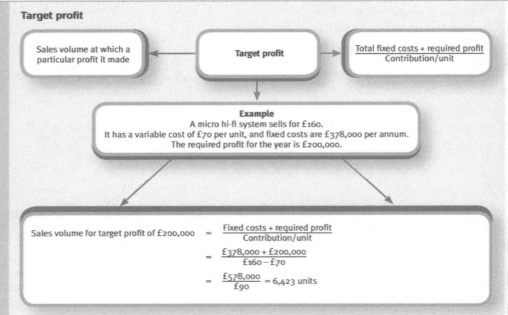

Target profit

Sales volume at which a particular profit it made ← **Target profit** → $\dfrac{\text{Total fixed costs + required profit}}{\text{Contribution/unit}}$

Example
A micro hi-fi system sells for £160.
It has a variable cost of £70 per unit, and fixed costs are £378,000 per annum.
The required profit for the year is £200,000.

$$\text{Sales volume for target profit of £200,000} = \dfrac{\text{Fixed costs + required profit}}{\text{Contribution/unit}}$$

$$= \dfrac{£378,000 + £200,000}{£160 - £70}$$

$$= \dfrac{£578,000}{£90} = 6,423 \text{ units}$$

Limiting factors

Definition

Key factor analysis is a technique used when we have one resource that is in scarce supply and we can make more than one type of product using that resource. Key factor analysis determines how to use this resource in such a way that profits are maximised.

Approach to key factor analysis

↓

(1) Determine the limiting factor or key factor that is in scarce supply

↓

(2) Calculate the contribution per unit generated by each product

↓

$$\frac{\text{Contribution per unit}}{\text{Number of units of scarce resource needed}} \longleftarrow$$ (3) Calculate the contribution per unit of scarce resource for each product

↓

(4) Select the product with the highest contribution per unit of scarce resource and make this first

Standard costing

Objective is to control the business:

1. Set up standard costs, prepare budgets and set targets.

2. Measure actual performance.

3. Compare actual v budget via variances.

4. Investigate reasons for differences and take action.

Types of standard:

- Ideal standards are based on optimal operating conditions with maximum efficiency and are usually unobtainable under normal conditions.

- Attainable standards are based on existing operating conditions.

- Basic standards are left unchanged from one period to another.

- Current standards are adjusted for each period.

Standard cost card

The standard cost card is a schedule that gives the standard costs that a unit of a product **should** incur.

Example	
	£
Materials (2kg at £3 per kg)	6
Labour (0.5 hours at £18 per hour)	9
Overheads (0.5 hours at £20 per hour)	10
Total standard cost per unit	25

Advantages of standard costing

- Comparison of actual costs to standard enables management to judge performance.

- Facilitates 'management by exception' – i.e. concentrate on investigating the most significant variances.

- Simplifies bookkeeping if Inventories are valued at standard.

Disadvantages of standard costing

- Standards can quickly become out of date.

- Establishing standards, monitoring of system and investigation of variances is costly.

- Unrealistic standards can demotivate staff.

Variance analysis – overview

Comparing like with like

When calculating variances it is vital that you compare like with like.

For each cost we compare the actual cost with how much it **should** have cost to produce the same actual level of output:

Actual cost

$\updownarrow$ Variance

Standard cost of
actual production

Materials variances

Materials Price variance

This is based on the actual quantity of materials purchased:

Materials purchased did cost

Actual quantity purchased $\times$ Actual price $= X$

Materials purchased should have cost

Actual quantity purchased $\times$ Standard price $= X$

} Price variance

Materials Usage variance

Quantity actually used at SP

Actual quantity used $\times$ Standard price $= X$

Quantity that should have been used at SP

Standard quantity used* $\times$ Standard price $= X$

} Usage variance

* i.e. quantity that should have been used to make actual output.

Reasons for variances

Price Variance

1. Wrong standards.
2. Lower/higher quality material.
3. Different supplier.
4. Good/poor purchasing.
5. External factors (inflation, exchange rates etc).

Usage Variance

1. Wrong standards.
2. Lower/higher quality of material.
3. Lower/higher quality of labour.
4. Theft.

Labour variances

Labour Rate variance

Hours paid did cost

Actual hours	x	Actual rate	=	X

Hours paid should have cost

Actual hours	x	Standard rate	=	X

} Rate variance

Labour Efficiency variance

Hours actually paid at SR

Actual hours	x	Standard rate	=	X

Hours that should have been paid at SR

Standard hours*	x	Standard rate	=	X

} Efficiency variance

* i.e. hours firm should have worked to make the actual output

Reasons for variances

Rate Variance

1. Wrong standards.
2. Wage inflation.
3. Lower/higher skilled employees.
4. Unplanned overtime or bonuses.

Efficiency variance

1. Wrong standards.
2. Lower/higher morale.
3. Lower/higher skilled employees.
4. Lower/higher quality of material.

Variable overhead variances

Variable overhead expenditure variance
Hours worked did cost
Actual hours worked   x   Actual rate   =   X
Hours worked should have cost   } Expenditure variance
Actual hours worked   x   Standard rate =   X

Variable overhead efficiency variance
Hours actually worked at SR
Actual hours worked   x   Standard rate =   X
Hours that should have been worked at SR   } Efficiency variance
Standard hours*   x   Standard rate =   X

* i.e. hours firm should have worked to make the actual output

Reasons for variances

Expenditure Variance	Efficiency variance
1. Wrong standards.	1. Wrong standards.
2. Rate inflation.	2. Lower/higher morale.
	3. Lower/higher skilled employees.
	4. Lower/higher quality of material.

Fixed overhead variances

Definition

The total fixed overhead variance is the difference between the actual fixed overhead, and the absorbed fixed overhead.

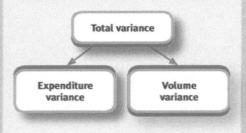

Fixed overhead expenditure variance (MC and TAC)

$$
\left.
\begin{array}{ll}
\text{Actual fixed overheads} & = X \\
\text{Budgeted fixed overheads} & = X
\end{array}
\right\} \text{Expenditure variance}
$$

Note: this is the original budget unadjusted for differences in output.

Fixed overhead volume variance (TAC only)

The volume variance is the difference between the budgeted overhead absorbed and the actual overhead absorbed.

$$
\left.
\begin{array}{lll}
\text{Budgeted production} & \times & \dfrac{\text{Standard cost}}{\text{per unit}} = X \\
\text{Actual production} & \times & \dfrac{\text{Standard cost}}{\text{per unit}} = X
\end{array}
\right\} \text{Volume var.}
$$

Reasons for fixed overhead variances

Fixed Overhead Expenditure Variance (MC and TAC)

The expenditure variance is the simplest fixed overhead variance and simply compares the original budgeted figure with actual. The variance will be due to poor budgeting or to a price rise.

e.g. rent increased by landlord.

Fixed Overhead Volume Variance (TAC)

The volume variance is due to the volume of production changing. A favourable (adverse) variance reflects the fact that more (less) units were made than planned. This could be due to:

- Poor budgeting.
- Labour efficiency.
- Availability of resources (e.g. shortage of materials).

Variance investigation

Variance calculations are just the starting point. Next, management need to decide which variances are worth investigating. To do this they will consider the following.

- How big is the variance?
  - Absolute size.
  - Relative size as a % of standard.
  - Overall trend.
- Is it favourable or adverse?
- Possible reasons for it.
  - Planning errors.
  - Measurement problems.
  - Random factors.
  - Operational issues.
- Controllability.
- Cost v benefit of investigation.
- Likelihood of a problem, based on past experience.

- The overall picture given by all the variances.

Management will seek to assign responsibility for the variances so they can be investigated further.

CBA focus

Performance appraisal is a very important topic. Two styles of task are commonplace:

Some tasks ask you to assess the organisation using ratios and other KPIs.

Some tasks give some new circumstances and require you to produce forecasts/revised ratios based on those changes.

Try to relate your comments to any details given in the scenario:

e.g. a switch to more expensive materials could explain changes in margins and quality.

Try to discuss both financial and non-financial indicators.

Performance measurement

An effective system of performance measurement is critical if the business is to be controlled.

Performance indicators can be:

- quantitative (i.e. expressed in numbers); or

- qualitative (i.e. not expressed in numbers). For example, satisfied/not satisfied or grade poor to excellent.

The 3Es

- **Economy** is the degree to which low prices were paid for the inputs of the business.

- **Effectiveness** is the degree to which the business objectives have been met.

- **Efficiency** is the relationship between inputs and outputs achieved, i.e. that as few inputs as possible have been used to achieve a particular output level of the desired quality.

Benchmarking

Need a suitable basis for comparison.

- Internal benchmarking. For example, by division.
- Competitive benchmarking.
- Activity (or process) benchmarking.
- Generic benchmarking – look at conceptually similar processes.

Profitability ratios

Return on capital employed (ROCE)

Capital employed is normally measured as non-current assets plus current assets less current liabilities and represents the long–term investment in the business. It is also measured as owners' capital plus long–term liabilities. Return on capital employed is frequently regarded as the best measure of profitability.

$$ROCE = \frac{\text{Profit before interest and taxation (PBIT)}}{\text{Capital employed}} \times 100\%$$

Note that the profit before interest is used, because the loan capital rewarded by that interest is included in capital employed.

A low return on capital employed (assets used) is caused by either a low profit margin or a low asset turnover or both. This can be seen by breaking down the primary ROCE ratio into its two components: profit margin and asset turnover.

$$\text{ROCE} = \frac{\text{PBIT}}{\text{Capital employed}}$$
$$= \frac{\text{PBIT}}{\text{Revenue}} \times \frac{\text{Revenue}}{\text{Capital employed}}$$
$$= \text{Profit margin} \times \text{Asset turnover}$$

Profit margin (on revenue)

$$\text{Profit margin} = \frac{\text{Profit before interest and taxation}}{\text{Revenue}} \times 100\%$$

A low margin indicates low selling prices or high costs or both.

Asset turnover

This will show the extent to which a company is utilising its assets to generate turnover:

$$\text{Asset turnover} = \frac{\text{Revenue}}{\text{Capital employed}}$$

A low turnover shows that a company is not generating a sufficient volume of business for the size of the asset base. This may be remedied by increasing sales or by disposing of some of the assets or both.

Gross profit margin

$$\text{Gross profit margin} = \frac{\text{Gross profit}}{\text{Revenue}} \times 100\%$$

The gross profit margin focuses on the trading account. A low margin could indicate selling prices too low or cost of sales too high.

Liquidity ratios

Current ratio

This indicates the extent to which the claims of short–term payables are covered by assets that are expected to be converted to cash.

$$\text{Current ratio} = \frac{\text{Current assets}}{\text{Current liabilities}}$$

Quick ratio (Acid test ratio)

This is calculated in the same way as the current ratio except that inventories are excluded from current assets, since they may not be converted into cash very quickly.

$$\text{Quick ratio} = \frac{\text{Current assets} - \text{inventory}}{\text{Current liabilities}}$$

This ratio is a much better test of immediate solvency.

Working capital ratios

Receivables collection period (Receivable days)

This is computed by dividing the receivables by the average daily sales to determine the number of days' sales held in receivables.

$$\text{Receivables collection period} = \frac{\text{Trade receivables}}{\text{Credit sales}} \times 365 \text{ days}$$

A long average collection period probably indicates poor credit control. If a company offers standard terms to its credit customers (e.g. 30 days credit), then the actual period of credit taken can be compared to the standard period.

Payables payment period

This is computed by dividing the payables by the average daily credit purchases to determine the number of days purchases held in payables. This tells us how long we are taking to pay our creditors. Too long a payment period may mean that they refuse to sell us goods in the future.

$$\text{Payables payment period} = \frac{\text{Trade payables}}{\text{Credit purchases}} \times 365 \text{ days}$$

Inventory holding period

This ratio indicates whether inventory levels are justified in relation to sales.

$$\text{Inventory holding period} = \frac{\text{Inventory}}{\text{Cost of sales}} \times 365 \text{ days}$$

Investor ratio

Gearing ratio

$$\text{Gearing ratio} = \text{Debt} / \text{Equity} \times 100$$

This ratio measures the proportion of assets invested in the business that are financed by borrowing.

A high gearing ratio means that the business is financed by a lot of debt, which can be dangerous. High levels of interest will be payable which the company may not be able to afford in a year of low profit.

The balanced scorecard

From strategic objectives to performance indicators

The balanced scorecard performance management system

	Financial perspective	Customer perspective	Internal business process perspective	Innovation and learning perspective
Strategic objective	Shareholder satisfaction	Customer satisfaction	Manufacturing excellence	New product innovation
CSF	Grow shareholder wealth	Achieve preferred supplier status	State-of-the-art process plant	Successful new product development
KPIs	• ROCE • Growth %	• Number of customer partnerships	• Cycle times • Unit cost • % yield	• % of revenues represented by new products

Lifecycle costing

All products go through lifecycles

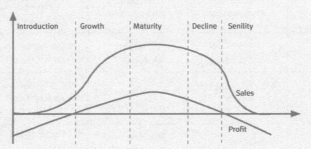

As shown by the difference between the revenue and cost curves, the pattern of costs over the lifecycle does not match that of revenue.

In particular, there will be high development costs during the introduction stage.

Traditional financial accounting has the following problems in this respect:

- It will look at the profit in a particular year, rather than assessing profitability over the whole lifecycle.

- Research costs are often written off in the year in which they are incurred rather than matching against (later) revenue.

KAPLAN PUBLISHING

Target costing

Many firms operate a 'cost-plus' pricing system, where the selling price of a product is calculated by adding a mark-up to the production cost.

Target costing is the reverse of this process:

1   The firm estimates the likely product price by looking at market conditions, competition, etc.

2   A target mark-up % is deducted from the price to give a target cost.

3   Production then sees if it can produce the product at the cost required.

 e.g

Example

R plc makes fridges. The current cost per unit is £100 and R sells them for £200, a mark-up of 100%. Due to increased competition, R feels that a selling price of £160 would be more competitive.

Assuming the mark up of 100% is still required, calculate the target cost.

Solution

Target price = £160

Target cost = 160 x 100/200 = £80

The production department needs to try to save £20 per unit on cost.

Activity Based Costing (ABC)

Step 1 Identify major activities.

Step 2 Identify appropriate cost drivers.

Step 3 Collect costs into pools based upon the activities (note: this is usually done for you in a question/task)

Step 4 Charge costs to units of production based on cost driver rate.

$$\text{Cost driver rate} = \frac{\text{Cost pool}}{\text{Level of cost driver}}$$

Examples of cost drivers

- Machine costs could be charged using machine hours.
- Quality control costs could be charged using number of inspections.
- Set-up costs could be charged using number of set-ups.

Benefits and Limitations of ABC

Benefits	Limitations
1. Provides more accurate product line costings.	1. Little evidence to date that ABC improves corporate profitability.
2. Is flexible enough to analyse costs by cost objects other than products, such as processes, areas of managerial responsibility and customers.	2. ABC information is historic and internally orientated and therefore lacks direct relevance for future strategic decisions.
3. Provides meaningful financial (periodic cost driver rates) and non-financial (periodic cost driver volume) measures.	3. Practical problems such as cost driver selection.
4. Aids identification and understanding of cost behaviour and thus has the potential to improve cost estimation.	
5. Provides a more logical, acceptable and comprehensible basis for costing work.	

Index